BIRDS OF THE NIGHT

Plate 1.—Male barn-owl with a field-vole under his talons. A flashlight photograph taken at night, in the interior of a barn.

BIRDS
OF THE NIGHT

By

ERIC J. HOSKING
F.R.P.S., M.B.O.U.

AND

CYRIL W. NEWBERRY
B.Sc., A.M.I.Mech.E., F.R.P.S.

With a Chapter on the
Eyes and Ears of Owls
by

STUART G. SMITH
B.Sc., PH.D.

Collins
FOURTEEN ST. JAMES'S PLACE, LONDON
1945

By the same Authors—

    INTIMATE SKETCHES FROM BIRD LIFE (*Country Life, 1940*)

    THE ART OF BIRD PHOTOGRAPHY (*Country Life, 1944*)

    BIRDS OF THE DAY (*Collins, 1944*)

In preparation—

    MORE BIRDS OF THE DAY

    THE SWALLOW

To Dorothy

PRINTED IN GREAT BRITAIN
COLLINS CLEAR-TYPE PRESS : LONDON AND GLASGOW
COPYRIGHT 1945

Contents

Illustrations

1. *Frontispiece.* Male barn-owl with a field-vole under his talons.
2. & 3. Profile of head of a barn-owl.
4. A snowy owl which alighted on a ship in the North Atlantic.
5. Owl pellets: left to right: little owl, long-eared owl, short-eared owl, tawny owl and barn-owl.
6. The barn-owl brings a field-vole to the nest.
7. A barn-owl with a young rat in its bill.
8. The barn-owl, photographed as it left its nesting hole.
9. Barn-owl with young. Note the food, a field-vole, by the side of the chicks.
10. Barn-owl carrying an adult field-vole in its bill.
11. Barn-owl brooding small young.
12. A barn-owl family. The cock is seen holding a field-vole in his bill: the hen has just given her vole to one of the chicks.
13. The hen barn-owl and family. Two field-voles may be seen by the side of the nest.
14. The barn-owl brings a field-vole to its young.
15. View of a Norfolk barn in which a pair of barn-owls nested.
16. As we entered the barn an owl flew out through the wicket-gate.
17. Interior of the barn, showing the bullock skep where barn-owls nested, and the hide used for photographing them.
18. The barn-owl, holding a common shrew under its talons, alighted at the wicket-gate.
19. The barn-owl perched on the side of a bullock skep.
20. Returning from an evening hunt, the barn-owl paused at the wicket-gate. The prey is part of a rat.
21. The barn-owl brings a rat as food for its young.
22. The cock barn-owl carrying a common shrew in his bill. The nest was situated in a bullock skep which was in the interior of a Norfolk barn.
23. Young barn-owls in their basket nest.

6

Preface

WHEN we first set out to present a selection of our bird photographs in book form, it was our intention to produce a volume of pictures each with a short descriptive text. We found that this worked out well in most cases, but that we could not fit the fascinating story of the owls into such a scheme. We have, for many years, spent a considerable amount of time in studying and photographing these little-known birds, and have recorded, in word and picture, many interesting details of their way of life. In view of this we could not do them justice within the limits of a few short passages and we felt that they merited a separate and distinct treatment.

So there came about the division of our work into two sections and eventually into two books. The selection of titles troubled us quite a lot until we hit on the matched pair, *Birds of the Day** and *Birds of the Night*; and even though we like these titles, we realise their limitations. Birds cannot easily be divided into any two such classes. Many of the diurnal birds are very active after dark, while some of the so-called nocturnal birds are by no means restricted to hunting at night. Perhaps the best-known example of this extended activity is the nightingale. Its very name associates it with the hours of darkness, but it cannot justly be termed "nocturnal." By day it lives the normal life of a diurnal bird—singing, feeding, and bringing up a family. It is more noticeable during the night because then its rich and vibrant song, continued at intervals during the hours of darkness, can be heard to advantage against the comparative quiet of the countryside. The sedge-warbler, too, is essentially a bird of the day, but its harsh chattering notes can often be heard through the stillness of a summer night. Indeed, in some parts we have found the sedge-warblers to provide a never-ending accompaniment as we have sat through the small hours in our quest of the owls.

So, *Birds of the Night* may conjure up different expectations from different readers. Some might expect to find the nightjar and the stone curlew included within its pages; and others might look for the woodcock and the shearwater; but all will probably agree that the first and obvious subjects are the owls, and, for better or worse, we have decided to limit the book to this important order of birds. Further than this, we are confining ourselves almost entirely to the five species of owls which nest regularly in the British Isles. There are others which turn up here occasionally, such as the eagle-owl, Tengmalm's owl, scops-owl and the hawk-owl ; lost wanderers driven from their courses by storms, and refugees from severe weather in their native haunts; but we have had little opportunity of studying them and will not pretend to write of them with authority. We will, however, just refer to one of them, the snowy owl, for, while it does not breed in

* Collins, 1944.

7

Plates 2 & 3.—Profile of a hea

these islands, it is a fairly regular winter visitor to the Shetlands and is often to be seen in the Orkneys and the Hebrides, and not infrequently in certain parts of the mainland of Scotland. It is a large white bird; a native of the arctic regions of Europe, Asia and North America; and there is little doubt that some individuals reach us each year by their own power of flight. There are, however, many instances of snowy owls alighting exhausted on ships in the North Atlantic and being brought to port in this way, and the specimen we illustrate was one of these that had been cared for by the sailors.

There is a good deal of mystery and superstition surrounding the owls, much of it due no doubt to the difficulty of making proper observations in the dark and

*a barn-owl (*daylight*).*

of learning the real facts about these birds. Where events are seen only indistinctly or incompletely, imagination is liable to come into play to fill in the missing details of the occurrence. For instance, there is little doubt that a large proportion of ghost stories can be attributed to owls, particularly the white—, or barn-owl, whose playground is often the churchyard or ruined building and whose eerie blood-curdling shriek and silent flight among the tombstones are quite unnerving to the inexperienced.

We have tried, in our account of the owls, to discount the effects of imagination and to give as true a picture as possible of the lives of these birds as we have seen them. We are sure of most of our facts, but where, because of

9

Plate 4.—A snowy owl which alighted on a ship in the North Atlantic (*daylight*).

darkness, or for some other reason, there is cause to doubt an observation that we have deemed of sufficient interest to include in our story, such doubt is indicated in the text so that readers may know what is reliable and what needs further confirmation.

Recent developments in optics and photography have assisted materially in the study of birds of the night and have given us great advantages over the ornithologists of a generation ago. The modern binocular, with its great light-gathering power, enables us, under twilight conditions, to see much detail that escapes the unaided eye; while the latest flash-bulbs and super-sensitive photographic plates record for us events that take place on even the darkest of nights.

Thus it is that, backed by the equipment that modern science has developed, we have been encouraged to go out in search of the owls. We have spent long periods with them—often into the small hours of the morning and right through the night—but we have found them fascinating in the extreme and, besides obtaining a unique series of pictures, we have been able to observe at close range some of the details of their life at the nest and have been privileged to obtain some records that are thought to be new to ornithology.

So much for our field work, but, fascinating as the owls are to watch, there is another side to their interesting story. They have the most wonderful eyesight and hearing to equip them for their nocturnal activities, and our friend, Dr. Stuart Smith, who has made a special study of the owls' eyes and ears, has contributed a masterly description of these organs. We are greatly indebted to him for his kindness in undertaking this task, and for reading through our manuscript, and also to his friend, Mr. Edward Bradbury, B.Sc., for his excellent drawings which illustrate the last chapter.

We cannot conclude this introduction without a mention of the very great help that has been so readily given by our publishers. On them has fallen much of the work of laying out this book, and they have carried through its production in the face of great difficulties inherent in wartime publishing. Finally we would add a word of admiration for the blockmakers, The Sun Engraving Co., whose skill has contributed so much to the appearance of this and its companion volume.

The General Characteristics of Owls

MORE than any other family of birds, the owls stand out as having certain well-defined and unmistakable characteristics by which they are easily recognised. They are predatory birds, hunting for the most part, though not exclusively, by night. They have the typical hooked bill and large talons of the predators, but differ from the diurnal birds of prey in having, in general, broad and rather flattened faces with large eyes, which, as in the case of man, are set in the front of the face and directed forwards. The size of the face is accentuated by a well-marked facial disk bounded by a ruff of short, stiff radiating feathers. It is largely this facial disk which gives the birds their characteristic appearance, but we should remark, in passing, that the disk is capable of very considerable control which may alter the facial expression out of all recognition. For instance, plates 71 and 72 shew two different phases of the tawny owl's expression, and the short-eared owl (plate 61) might well be a different bird from that of plate 65, though it is, in fact, the same. In general, the facial disk held right forward as in plate 58 indicates an aggressive or excited mood, while the expression of plate 52, for example, marks a period of relaxation and tranquillity.

In all the owls, the head appears to rest directly on the shoulders. This, however, is deceptive and is due to the masking of the neck by the plentiful soft plumage. The neck is, in fact, rather long, and the bird is able to turn its head through an unusually large angle. This great mobility of the head is very necessary as it compensates the owl for a very restricted mobility of the eye, which organ is, in fact, fixed in the socket; but it is, in many ways, as Dr. Stuart Smith explains in Chapter 7, a most remarkable instrument of vision, and merits the almost legendary powers that popular belief attributes to it.

Not only in their visual sensitivity are the owls specially adapted for their nocturnal activities. They have very large ears affording them a keen sense of hearing, and in this they are aided by the special accomplishment of having a silent flight, made possible by the softness of their feathers. Although an owl will drop from a perch to seize a rodent or other prey passing underneath, the majority of its hunting is done on the wing. The owls' characteristic method is to fly steadily, usually some ten or twenty feet above the ground, beating along the side of a hedge or quartering the woods, open fields, marsh or moorland, according to which particular species is concerned; and in this active manner of seeking a timid prey in the quiet stillness of the dusk, a silent flight is a very great advantage to the owls. They are able to listen for the rustle of a rodent in the herbage as well as seek him with their eyes, and, at the same time, they do not reveal their own presence and so frighten their prey as they would if their approach flight were noisy.

The owls' method of feeding is of interest. Unlike most other predatory

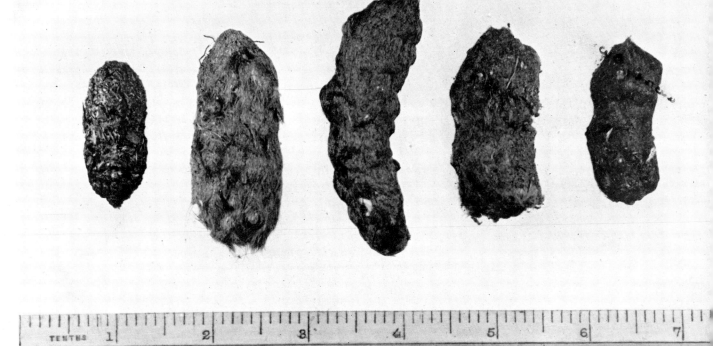

Plate 5.—Owl pellets : left to right: little owl, long-eared owl, short-eared owl, tawny owl and barn-owl.

birds, the owls do not pluck and dismember their prey, but generally swallow it whole; fur, feathers and all. The indigestible matter is subsequently disgorged in the form of pellets of closely compacted material. These pellets, which are illustrated in plate 5, are often dropped near a roosting place or a nest, and are a useful indication of the likely presence of an owl in the vicinity; and, what is more, they serve to reveal a good deal of information about the owls' diet. By dissecting them we are able to find the bones of vertebrate prey and the hard scaly parts of invertebrates. The wing cases of beetles and the pincers of ear-wigs, for example, enable us to count the number of items that have been consumed.

Although they use somewhat diverse nesting sites, the owls have one trait in common in the matter of nesting. They like to find a site ready made for them as, with few half-hearted exceptions, they make no attempt at nest-building themselves. They use holes, ledges in old buildings, the nests of other large birds, and even nest on the ground, laying their eggs directly on the "floor" or bottom of the hole without the addition of any nest lining.

The eggs of all the owls are white, and are generally laid at intervals of two days, though we have noted many divergencies from this. The clutch is usually from three to five, but this may vary considerably, particularly in the case of the short-eared owl, which lays much larger clutches when food is very plenti-

13

ful. After about four weeks' incubation the young are hatched out blind, and covered with whitish down. They have long fledging periods, ranging from about four weeks in most cases to about nine or ten weeks for the barn owl, and they seem to be dependent on their parents for some time after they can fly. They remain in the vicinity of the nest for a considerable time; in fact, most of our British owls can be regarded as sedentary, and only the short-eared shews much tendency to migrate.

There is still a great deal to be discovered about the lives and habits of the owls, and, by way of stimulating an interest in these important birds, we have set down some of our findings in the succeeding chapters. Our observations are continuing, however, as and when opportunities occur, and in course of time we hope to enlarge on what we have written here and to prepare a monograph on the British Owls. To that end we shall welcome any original observations that readers may care to send us in order that the work shall represent as fully as possible the life stories of these birds of the night.

The Barn-Owl

THE WHITE-BREASTED BARN-OWL is, perhaps, the best-known of our native owls, for it shews a particular predisposition to associate with man. Whilst not abundant anywhere, it is to be found in most parts of the British Isles, haunting the vicinity of farms and ruined buildings. Its favourite roosts and nesting sites are in dark, sheltered nooks in barns and such-like places, though it is also to be found in woodlands where it makes use of hollow trees.

The bird is largely nocturnal, hunting at dusk and during the night, and roosting in some sheltered place during the daytime, but it is sometimes to be seen about by day, especially on fine winter afternoons. It is easily recognised and distinguished from the other owls by its very light—practically pure white —face, breast, and underparts. Seen in flight, it appears, indeed, to be a white bird, but the back and wings are actually a buff colour beautifully mottled with grey. There is a dark-breasted variety, which is native on the Continent and which occurs occasionally in these islands, and closely allied forms are to be found in almost every country in the world, so that the barn-owl may be considered almost cosmopolitan in range and is certainly the most widely-distributed land bird that exists.

Our first attempt at the photography of a nocturnal bird by flashlight was made on a barn-owl in 1936. It was rather in the nature of an experiment and an adventure for, so far as we knew, very little of this work had been attempted, and we had nothing to guide us in the technique we should use or the results to be expected.

The nest, with three eggs, was discovered in a hole in the gnarled trunk of an old oak tree on May 5th. The hen was sitting at the time, but this could not be taken to mean the clutch was complete as it is usual with many of the birds of prey for incubation to begin as soon as the first egg is laid. There were in fact, two more eggs, making five in all when we next visited the nest on May 10th. Periodic visits were made to the nest while the hen was incubating the eggs and we noted that the first egg hatched on May 28th. The second followed a day later, and all five chicks were out of their shells by June 4th.

We made careful preparations to begin photography and, about the end of the month, we began the erection of a hide from which the camera could be operated. This construction, consisting of a platform at the required height with a screen of hessian to conceal us from the bird, has been fully described in one of our earlier books, *The Art of Bird Photography* (Country Life 1944), so need not be repeated here. The flashlight apparatus was fixed to the front of the hide with flexible wire connections to the inside so that the flash could be fired from our

Plate 6.—The barn-owl brings a field-vole to the nest (*flashlight*).

Plate 7.—A barn-owl with a young rat in its bill (*flashlight*).

position of hiding ; and the whole erection was then left for several days for the owls to become accustomed to its presence.

At last the time came when we considered it expedient to begin close-up observation and photography so, choosing the period a little before dusk for our approach, we set out for the hide.

It was a fine, still, summer evening as we made our way across the fields. The thrill of that first sortie in quest of an owl by flashlight will not easily be forgotten and we recall how the sight of that nesting hole and hide keyed us up to a high pitch of expectancy. Careful as our preparations had been, there were still many doubts in our minds. Primarily, how would the birds themselves react? Would

16

they be frightened and put off by the flash? Or would the flash itself fail us at the critical moment? Our wonderings were soon cut short, however, by our arrival at the hide and the need for getting ourselves installed with the minimum of delay or fuss. Everything was soon in order and we settled down in the hide to begin the first spell of what was to prove the most absorbing and fascinating branch of bird photography.

We glanced at the time and made the first record in the notebook. It was 9.40 p.m. B.S.T. and, though the light outside was still fairly good and we could see the nesting hole quite clearly, it was rather dark inside the hide and we quickly found some difficulty in taking notes. Writing in the dark proved, indeed, to be our most intractable problem and even to this day we have not mastered it to our satisfaction.

During these first minutes in the owl hide we experienced a remarkable sensation; a feeling of being apart from the world; of standing on the threshold of some vast uncharted realm. The tense expectancy of something—we knew

Plate 8.—The barn-owl, photographed as it left its nesting-hole (*flashlight*).

not quite what to expect—was heightened by the quiet stillness of the summer twilight; that enchanting interlude that belongs neither to the day nor yet to the night. We peered out of the peep-hole at the tree in front of us. The colour was going from its mossy, deeply-creviced bark, and everything was taking on the sombre grey mantle that seems to clothe the world during the hours of darkness.

We sat there with the shutter release and the switch for the flashlight held ready for action. Minutes passed very slowly, but the darkness deepened inexorably. Our task clearly called for persistence in the early stages, but the novelty of it, coupled with an irrepressible optimism in the outcome, kept us in the hide, and soon we were rewarded with a first close-up view of our quarry.

Without any warning of its approach, a white shape flashed in front of us. The tension of waiting surged to a sudden climax, and our hearts beat fast as we peered out from the hide, eagerly striving in the dim light to take in every detail of the fleeting spectacle. We could make out the barn-owl perched at the entrance to the nest. Her back was towards us; the long reach of her folded wings almost covered her tail. Instinctively, fingers tightened on the shutter release, but, for a matter of seconds, that seemed, however, more like an age, she remained motionless without shewing her face. We held our breath and watched, spell-bound, until, disturbed perhaps by some slight noise, she turned and looked at the hide. This was the moment we had waited for.

That first flash at an owl was itself a startling experience. Obvious as it seems now, we had not foreseen that the period of staring into the darkness had left our eyes in no condition to withstand the intense light of a flash-bulb. We had a momentary impression of the owl, but it was quickly followed by an impenetrable green veil which persisted for some while. Nothing seemed to dispel it and we wondered at first whether we had caused some permanent injury to our eyes, but, after a time, things gradually became more normal again and we were very greatly relieved. Our first glance was out of the hide and, to our surprise, we saw the barn-owl still sitting where she had been when we took the photograph. She appeared to be quite unconcerned, though we wondered whether she, too, had been temporarily blinded.

Shortly after this she flew from the nest and we half expected that we should see no more of her that evening, but nevertheless, full of optimism, we changed the spent flash-bulb for a new one and settled down to await events. The night was now becoming very dark and we could barely discern the nesting hole some six feet in front of us but, fortunately, the light colour of the barn-owl's plumage helped us to see when she returned.

The next visit to the nest was much the same as the first one. The bird arrived absolutely silently and there was barely a sound even of her claws scratching at

18

Plate 9.—Barn-owl with young. Note the food, a field-vole, by the side of the chicks (*flashlight*).

the bark of the tree. We fired the flash when we thought she was in a suitable attitude, but this time took the precaution of closing our eyes at the instant of firing. It helped considerably and, though there was a small effect of dazzle, we were able to see almost at once that the owl was still there.

After she had left, we inserted yet another flash-bulb and had hardly done so when an owl arrived on the oak and went straight down into the nest. Whether it was the bird that had just left, or whether it was the other one of the pair, we are unable to say, and neither could we see whether any food was carried. We waited, peering anxiously into the darkness, and presently discerned a head and shoulders appearing from the hole. The temptation was too great to

[*Continued on page 21.*

Plate 10.—Barn-owl carrying an adult field-vole in its bill (*flashlight*).

20

resist and, fired with enthusiasm for this new adventure, we let off another flash.

The owls paid two more visits to the nest before midnight, when we vacated the hide. It was, by then, quite impossible to see anything of what was taking place, and we felt that little was to be gained by further waiting during the hours of darkness. We should have liked to have waited for the dawn but, having other tasks on hand for the next day, we considered discretion to be the better part of valour and returned to our lodgings for a few hours in bed.

The following evening we returned to the hide about 9 o'clock. It was dull and cloudy after a very wet day and, possibly because of this change in the weather, our success of the previous night was not repeated. The owls were visiting the nest at much longer intervals and we thought that they must have been finding difficulty in hunting. We have noticed the same thing on other occasions since then, particularly in the case of the buzzard and golden eagle, and concluded that furry creatures, which comprise a large part of the prey of these birds, do not like getting their fur wet and, in consequence, stay much more under cover when the herbage is saturated. Anyway, whatever the cause may have been, we saw only two visits of the owls during a vigil of three and a half hours.

Nothing daunted, we tried again the next night. There had been more heavy rain during the day but the evening was clear, and soon the stars were twinkling in all their brilliance. It was, however, 10.20 p.m. before the first owl returned. She came silently as before, perched at the entrance to the nest and dropped something from her bill. In the poor light we could not be sure of the identity of her prey though it appeared to be a rat. The old owl did not go down into the nest, neither did she remain long at the hole. It appeared that the young were old enough by now to feed themselves and the parents were anxious to be off to continue the hunt for more prey.

Four visits of the old birds were made during this spell of watching but only once did one of the birds go right into the hole, pausing long enough at the entrance on this occasion to enable us to take a photograph. This was one of our lucky nights, for, though we did not realise it at the time of making the exposure, the bird was still holding a rat and we had secured our first picture (and possibly the first ever to be taken by flashlight) of an owl with prey (plate 7).

For the next few seasons our flashlight technique was directed to other owls, so that it was 1942 before we had an opportunity to photograph the barn-owl again. The nest was much more interesting than the previous one as, being on the floor of a small attic-like space over a pig-sty, it was accessible and could be kept under observation. It was found on June 10th when it contained five eggs. "Contained" is perhaps not the best word to use on this occasion as the barn-owl builds no nest in which her eggs could be contained. They were merely laid on the floor. At this date one would have expected the eggs to be hard set, but examination by the light of a torch revealed them as being fairly fresh.

Periodic visits were paid to the nest, but, beyond observing the cock on several occasions carrying food to the sitting hen, we had nothing to record till July 2nd when one of the chicks was found to be hatched. Increased attention was now paid to this nest and a start was made with the construction of a hide. Two young were hatched by the evening of the 3rd. They were quaint little creatures, covered in greyish-white down, with pinched-looking faces tapering downwards to the prominent hooked bill. Their eyes were not yet opened, though even at this stage, the length of the eyelids gave an indication of the remarkable organs of sight with which these birds are endowed. There were still only two young on the evening of the 4th when we visited the nest to erect the flashlight apparatus, but on the afternoon of the 8th, four of them were hatched and were cheeping vigorously.

The next day, the fifth egg was nearly hatched and the chick could be heard cheeping from inside the shell. On this occasion there was, for the first time, some food lying beside the nest. It consisted of an adult field-vole and a mouse. We cut off their tails so that we should not count the same ones again should they still be there on our next visit. This practice has proved very valuable in our efforts to keep records of the food of predatory birds, and we commend it to others who may have the same problems on hand. By the evening of the following day, July 10th, the fifth egg had hatched but the pieces of egg shell were still in the nest. The field-vole of the previous day had disappeared, but the mouse was still exactly as we had left it and no other food appeared to have been brought. We spent 2½ hours at the nest on this occasion and during the first part of the time while the parent owl was still away, the young kept up a continual "chittering," which seemed to be a call to their mother to come and brood them. We noted too, that the eldest chick, now 8 days old, was beginning to develop an occasional snore, a note which we later identified as a call for food. The hen returned after about 50 minutes and settled to brood the young, at which they all became quite silent and probably went to sleep. No food was brought in during our watch and there was, in fact, very little activity of any kind to record. The young, it seemed, were still at the stage when they did little else than sleep.

On our next visit, two days later, we found the barn-owl family reduced to three. The youngest chick had died and its body had been thrown or carried some feet away from the nest, and one of the others was missing altogether. We were never able to discover what had happened to these two, but such thinning of the brood by natural causes is not uncommon in the avian world—in fact, it is necessary in order to prevent a state of overcrowding.

There were four fresh field-voles by the nest and we had seen the cock barn-owl still busy hunting as we approached the pig-sty, so presumably the young

Plate 11.—Barn-owl brooding small young (*flashlight*).

were now beginning to develop appetites. The eldest was 10 days old. Field-voles seemed to be the predominant food at this stage, and practically nothing else was brought to the nest, although rats and mice were common in and around the farm buildings. The cock barn-owl did most of the hunting while the hen was occupied in brooding the chicks. He would sail in through the doorway of the sty with a sweeping glide, bringing him up to one of the roof beams above the attic floor. Here, framed within the angle of the roof, he made a splendid picture, and we were delighted to find that he was even less nervous of the flashlight than was his mate, and she took very little notice of it after the first few times.

Sometimes, still holding the vole in his bill, he would fly down from his perch

Plate 12.—A barn-owl family. The cock is seen holding a field-vole in his bill ; the hen has just given her vole to one of the chicks (*flashlight*).

on the beam and deposit his prey by the side of the nest or give it direct to the sitting hen; but sometimes he would call her softly and she would leave the nest and go to join him on the beam, where, after a few moments' soft conversational twitter, he would pass the vole to her for her to bring it the last stage to the nest. By July 15th, that is, when the youngest surviving chick was a week old, the hen as well as the cock was spending some time in hunting, and at one of the visits, when the two birds returned together to the attic, there took place a remarkable vocal display of indescribable notes and calls which, at the time, not being able to see the birds, we could not interpret, but which we were subsequently able to identify as a courtship display. When the birds came into our view, we saw

Plate 13.—The hen barn-owl and family. Two field-voles may be seen by the side of the nest (*flashlight*).

that they were each carrying a vole which they brought and put down by the nest. The young were, by this time, growing very quickly but they were still all covered in greyish-white down. They were, however, beginning to feed themselves and we suspected that they were able to swallow young voles complete though, in the darkness of the attic, it was difficult to see this point for certain.

The following evening was warm and dry and seemed good for hunting, and, possibly influenced by this as well as by the growth of the chicks, the hen barn-owl spent no time brooding them during the whole of our watch. She took a share with her mate in collecting food for the growing family and came back three times against his five during our spell in the hide. We noticed that all the

 [*Continued on page 27.*

Plate 14.—The barn-owl brings a field-vole to its young (*flashlight*).

26

prey consisted of field-voles, and that whereas the cock barn owl was bringing mostly adult voles, the hen was bringing half- to three-quarter-grown ones. Both birds normally carried the prey in their left talons during flight, but they generally passed it up to the bill just before alighting, presumably to leave both feet free for perching. This procedure was by no means invariable, however, and, in the frontispiece, we illustrate the cock still holding a vole in his talons when he alighted on a beam. It will be noticed that he holds the vole in his left talons and balances on the right leg by swinging the body and tail over to that side.

Although these owls usually began their hunting about sunset and continued through the hours of darkness, we noticed that they were considerably influenced by the weather. As we remarked earlier, rodents, which are the chief food of these birds, seem to stay under cover when the ground is wet; and on several occasions we found that the owls anticipated the approach of rain by laying in a small store of rodents even if this meant hunting in broad daylight. Thus, one day at 4 p.m. B.D.S.T., we saw the owls abroad and watched them hunting for some time; and when, later that evening, we visited the hide, there were several voles lying by the nest. The weather had by then deteriorated and it was raining and blowing hard. The wind was penetrating right into the attic space, and dust and pieces were swirling up from the floor in little eddies. The young barn-owls must have been feeling the cold in spite of their thick covering of down, for their "chittering" note was much more in evidence than for some time past, and we had not been long in the hide when the hen returned without bringing any food. She settled to brood the young, and continued to do so during the whole of our stay, and we concluded that hunting was out of the question as we saw nothing of the cock bird during that evening.

The bad weather continued through the next day with a brief respite about tea time, and it seems that the owls must have taken advantage of this lull to hunt, for there were three voles—one still warm—when we arrived at the hide that evening. Again we saw no food brought during the whole of our vigil, and the hen sat by the chicks, though on this occasion she did not brood them, but merely shielded them from the draught.

These, and other spells of daylight hunting gave us an excellent opportunity of seeing something of this phase of the owls' life and we were surprised to find how large an area of ground is covered by these birds. Cycling along a track across the marshes one afternoon we saw a barn-owl which, because of its un-usually light colouring, we were soon able to recognise as "our" cock. We watched him beating leisurely across the marsh, some twelve or fifteen feet above the ground, when suddenly he swung upwards and back, and dived down to the ground where he remained for some minutes. When he rose again in flight he was not carrying any food, but he may, of course, have caught something and swallowed it. There certainly would have been time. He continued hunting, and

27

Plate 15.—View of a Norfolk barn in which a pair of barn-owls nested.

a little farther on he hesitated again and dropped down. We saw him fluttering along the ground as if chasing something, but unfortunately the long grass prevented us from having a clear view. Soon he flew up and alighted on the topmost branch of a hawthorn tree. He sat for a little while, gazing around him, and, curiously enough, although there were numerous small birds flitting about the nearby bushes, not one of them made any attempt to mob him, as small birds usually do the birds of prey.

His next move was to beat along a hedgerow fringing the marsh. He flew in our direction and was barely a hundred yards from us when we saw him pounce again. This time he certainly was successful, for he rose clutching something

Plate 16.—As we entered the barn an owl flew out through the wicket-gate (*daylight*).

close under his body. Away over the marsh he flew, and here the peewits and redshanks mobbed him viciously, but he went on without faltering or deviating from his course and made a bee-line for the farm where our hide was erected. This confirmed that we were not mistaken as to his identity, and, when we checked up the distance afterwards, we found that he had been hunting a full mile from his nesting site.

Again and again we had opportunities of watching this bird on the wing and we found that the instance recorded above was not exceptional. His hunting ground must have covered quite three or four square miles. He did not, however, always utilize the whole area and did a considerable part of his foraging within

29

a short distance of the nest. He must have been a great asset to the farmer on whose land he was resident.

Much as we should have liked to watch these barn-owls throughout the fledging of the young, we were unable to stay in the vicinity for the ten or twelve weeks that the young spend in and about the nest before they fly. We had to leave them when they were about four weeks old, by which time they were quite large and very lively, but were only just beginning to feather. We kept in touch, however, with the farmer and presently learned, to our satisfaction, that all three of the young barn-owls had left the nest safely.

The following year we had another opportunity of watching what we believed to be the same pair of barn-owls. We were at the farm where they had nested previously, when we saw one of them fly into a large barn not far from the site of last year's nest. Following up this clue, we searched the barn and, in several places, noticed numerous droppings under what were obviously favourite perches, so we knew the barn-owls must be using the barn a good deal. Imagine our surprise, however, when we discovered the nest, not in a dark nook as we expected, but in a bullock skep, that is, a wicker basket some four feet by three feet, and about three feet deep, which, being not required at this season of the year, had been thrown up out of the way at one end of the barn, and, together with a roll of wire netting and other odds and ends of farm equipment, was wedged behind the upturned shafts of a cart.

There were two eggs lying among a few pellets when we first saw the nest on April 24th. Four days later we found that there were three eggs, and on May 1st the clutch was complete with four. When visiting the barn at this period, we noticed that both owls were usually to be found there. The cock, who was probably roosting on one of the roof beams, would fly out through a wicket gate high in one end wall as soon as we entered the barn, but the hen, who was brooding her eggs, would sit tight until we touched the skep, when she, too, would follow her mate out through the wicket.

Incubation continued, and, with the passing days, the number of pellets littering the skep steadily increased. By the time the first egg hatched, on May 22nd, there must have been between thirty and forty.

The second egg was hatched on May 23rd, and when we next visited the nest on the 29th, the third chick was hatched. It was, by then, dry and quite active and must have been out of the shell for a day or two, though both pieces of shell were still lying in the nest. We noticed, too, on this occasion, that there were three young rats and four field-voles in the skep—the first food we had seen there. The following day, the fourth and last egg hatched and, reckoning back to the laying dates, we noted that the incubation period was only thirty days compared with the period of thirty two to thirty-four days recorded in the *Handbook of British Birds* as normal for the barn-owl.

 [*Continued on page* 32.

Plate 17.—Interior of the barn, showing the bullock skep where barn-owls nested, and the hide used for photographing them.

We built our hide and soon started a period of intensive watching, visiting the barn most evenings about an hour before sunset and staying for periods ranging from two hours up to about ten hours. This covered the normal active period of the owls, although they not infrequently did a little hunting during the late afternoon or early evening.

As we sat in the hide, facing the nest, the wicket gate was away to our left at the far end of the barn, and the evening light flooded in through the opening. The tie-beams in the roof lay there, one beyond the other, silhouetted against the distant glow. The light was not very good inside the wicker skep, but we could make out the greyish-white, downy forms of the young owls huddled together near the back of the basket. They lay still but kept up a continuous chorus of "chittering."

Presently a dark form appeared in the opening of the wicket gate and was very conspicuous against the brightness outside. It was the hen barn-owl. She flew on to one of the cross beams and sat looking about her for a few minutes. The extreme flexibility of the neck was very evident, with the head turning in almost every direction while the body was not moved perceptibly. Satisfied with her inspection, she soon launched herself downwards from her perch, and, with a single sweep of silent flight, moved to a beam nearer the nest. After another pause to look about again, especially at the nest and the hide, she flew on to the top of the skep and then down into it. In the darkness her white face and breast shewed up clearly as she turned to face us, and we had a good impression of her large, dark, but lustrous, eyes.

She brooded the young for a time, seeming somewhat suspicious of the hide, and the inevitable slight creakings which emanated from it. She stood up after a little while, walked up to the front of the skep, and from there flew up to a nearby beam from which she scrutinised the hide and seemed to look right through it. She called softly on occasions and presently another dark shape appeared at the wicket, and the cock flew into the barn, carrying a field-vole in his bill. He joined his mate on the beam, settling a little way from her, and we had our first glimpse of the display of these birds.

Step by step the cock sidled up to the hen, shaking himself a little and ruffling his feathers as he did so, until, when he was quite close to her, he turned and rubbed his face against her head. He appeared almost as if he were offering her the field-vole, but she did not accept it and, after sitting by her side for a little while, he flew down to the nest where he deposited the vole and went off to do some more hunting.

We soon discovered that the situation of this nest in the large, comparatively light, barn was to make our work more trying and difficult than usual, for, even when not at the nest, the owls spent considerable periods inside the barn and we had, during such times, to keep perfectly quiet and still when, in other circum-

32

[Continued on page 34.

Plate 18.—The barn-owl, holding a common shrew under its talons, alighted at the wicket-gate (*flashlight*).

stances, we might have been able to relax a little. This enforced concentration had its rewards, however, for we were able to see considerably more of the owls than at any other nest we have had under observation. For instance, it was only two days after our first glimpse of the display recorded above that, in company with Dr. Stuart Smith, we saw an even more complete performance.

It was just before sunset when the cock barn-owl arrived back in the barn. He sailed in, a silent, ghost-like figure in the half-light, and alighted, with hardly a scratch, on one of the beams quite near the nest and hide. The hen followed almost at once and settled by him and we noted that neither bird brought any prey. They sat there looking around them for a few moments, and then the cock, on a sudden impulse, flew down to the nest and glanced at the young. It was a brief visit, however, and almost immediately he rejoined the hen on the beam, settling about a foot away from her and, like her, facing towards our end of the barn. Both birds then engaged in a twittering "conversation" accompanied by beak-snapping, after which the cock slowly stretched his head and neck upwards and puffed out his feathers. He looked grotesque with his head thrown well back and his beak open wide. The hen quivered a little, and the cock began to sway his head from side to side, and presently to wave it with a somewhat circular motion. The hen started to sway in sympathy and to utter a snoring note as she did so, and, at the same time, she edged up until she was close beside the cock. He then retracted his neck and lowered his head, and the two birds rubbed cheeks together. They followed this by a short bout of clicking their bills together, but the cock soon brought this to an end by seizing the hen by the neck feathers and swaying her from side to side. She appeared to enjoy this seeming rough treatment and purred intermittently during the course of it, but gradually the activity subsided until the two birds were merely standing there, side by side. They remained thus for a little while and then both flew from the barn as if to resume hunting.

Much of the procedure at this nest was very similar to what we have already described. Field-voles, with an occasional mouse, mole, or shrew, formed the entire diet of the young for the first two or three weeks, but we noticed later that, as the young grew, their diet was increased to include young rats. At first the rats were decapitated before being brought to the nest, presumably because the young owls would have been unable to cope with the skulls, but later even this precaution was dispensed with and the young owls seemed to be able to swallow whatever was brought to them. Several times, in the course of all-night watches, we found a tendency for the food brought in to vary as the night progressed. Field-voles formed the first course and seemed plentiful during the period around sunset and for some time after, but later in the night the owls were bringing in more rats. Was this variation related to the owls' habits, we wondered. It may

34 [*Continued on page* 37.

Plate 19.—The barn-owl perched on the side of a bullock skep (*flashlight*).

Plate 20.—Returning from an evening hunt, the barn-owl paused at the wicket-gate. The prey is part of a rat (*flashlight*).

Plate 21.—The barn-owl brings a rat as food for its young (*flashlight*).

be, for the owls are particularly active about dusk and could readily catch voles, whereas later in the night they tend to sit about in barns and such places and would notice the rats moving about beneath them. Shrews and long-tailed field-mice seemed to appear only on very dark or moonless nights.

The situation of this nest in the skep gave us an excellent opportunity for watching the development of the young owls. The first stage, when they were covered in short greyish-white down and had rather pinched, wizened faces, lasted about a fortnight. During this time they were brooded by the hen for the greater part of the time and were fed by her.

In the course of their third week there was a marked change in their appear-

Plate 22.—The cock barn-owl carrying a common shrew in his bill. The nest was situated in a bullock skep which was in the interior of a Norfolk barn (*flashlight*).

ance. The first, short down was replaced by longer, thicker down, almost pure white in colour, and the young, gaining strength, were able to sit up. They began to develop a loud snoring note which seemed to indicate hunger and, at 17 days old, they could swallow small voles that were offered to them by their parents. When 25 days old, the chicks were becoming quite lively. They would run to meet the cock as he came back into the skep and, taking the food from him, swallowed it whole with little difficulty.

They were about four weeks old when they began to show signs of feathering, the feathers appearing along the edges of the wings and the tail. At this stage the facial disks were broadening and becoming whiter, and the youngsters were

38   [*Continued on page* 40.

Plate 23.—Young barn-owls in their basket-nest (*flashlight*).

39

growing more attractive to look at. They were developing an element of individuality and about this time we saw the first squabble over food. Two of the owlets were disputing the possession of a vole that had been brought in and left by the cock. Each tried to intimidate the other by a mild threat display, comprising posing in grotesque attitudes, glaring, and finally swaying the body from side to side. Eventually one of the chicks, apparently the acknowledged winner, seized the food, carried it off to a remote part of the basket, and, with its back turned towards the others, proceeded to swallow the prize.

The following week saw a great increase in the activities of the young. They were constantly walking about the skep and even trying to climb up it, and energetic wing-flapping was part of their regular routine. They greeted their parents eagerly and snatched at food as soon as it was brought, so that from this time onwards we had great difficulty in keeping even an approximate record of their diet.

At seven weeks, the young appeared almost as large as their parents. The wing primaries and tail feathers were developing rapidly, though their bodies were still largely clad in the profuse white down. In this condition, the age difference between the young was very clearly apparent as may be seen in plate 25, which shews, from left to right, the youngest, the eldest, the second eldest and the third eldest; there being ten days' difference between the eldest and the youngest.

Soon after this, the eldest was making his first attempt at flight. He would come out to the front of the skep and look around, particularly up towards the wicket gate for signs of his parents, and, if food was not forthcoming he would pass the time by fluttering about the interior of the basket. Feather development at this stage was very rapid and a lot of down was shaken loose by these attempts at flight and by the vigorous wing-flapping that was indulged in repeatedly.

Again we were unable to stay with these owls for the whole of their fledging period, but before leaving them, we arranged for two of the local farm hands to watch for the young owls' first flight. It seems that they missed this event for their dates did not agree; but we do at least know that the youngsters got safely off the nest.

Looking back through our notes, we find that, during our spells of watching, the parent owls brought back to the nest no less than 91 short-tailed field-voles and 21 rats, and we also have records of 8 common shrews, 2 long-tailed field-mice, 1 mole, and 1 pigmy shrew. This bag alone shews the barn-owl to be a most helpful species of bird in ridding the countryside of these vermin, but the list is far from complete and, in the course of bringing up a family, the barn-owl must destroy many times this number of voles and rats. It should, therefore, be left unmolested, or even encouraged, where possible, by the provision of suitable large nesting-boxes.

Plate 24.—Young barn-owls. The owlet in the middle is swallowing a field-vole (*flashlight*).

Plate 25.—Young barn-owls. Note the difference in their ages. The youngest is on the left,
next comes the oldest, then the second oldest, and finally the second youngest (*flashlight*).

The Little Owl

UNTIL the middle of the nineteenth century, the little owl occurred in the British Isles only as a rare and occasional visitor. Its native haunts were across the Channel, where it had a range extending from the Low Countries, France, and the Iberian Peninsula, through Central Europe and the lands fringing the Mediterranean, to Egypt and south-west Asia. In these parts it had acquired the reputation of being a good friend of the gardener and agriculturist on account of its habit of feeding upon insects, reptiles, and small rodents, and for this reason, attempts were made, beginning about the middle of the century, to introduce the bird to this country.

The first known experiment was about 1843 when Charles Waterton imported some little owls from Rome and released them in Walton Park, Yorkshire, but this effort appears to have been unsuccessful. Other attempts followed, without success, until, in 1879, Mr. E. G. B. Meade-Waldo, after several importations from Holland, recorded a pair breeding at Edenbridge, Kent; and in 1889, Lord Lilford, who had also tried several times to establish the species in Northamptonshire, found a nest near Oundle. From these two centres, the little owl multiplied and spread gradually outwards into the surrounding country. Once it really got a hold, the bird seemed to find conditions to its liking, for it increased its range year by year. It is now to be found over practically the whole of England and Wales except Anglesey and those counties north of Lancashire and Yorkshire; and there are indications that it is still extending its range.

The country most favoured by the little owl is open grass or agricultural land, so long as there are a few trees here and there such as occur in parklands and in old hedgerows. The bird may, however, be found in treeless wastes and among sand-dunes.

The nest is usually in a hole. It may be, and most often is, a hole in a tree; but holes in walls and ruined buildings may be used; and the bird not infrequently nests in rabbit-burrows. We illustrate, in plates 29, 34, 28, and 30, four typical nesting-sites of the little owl. The first is deep in a hollow between the roots of an old oak tree, the broken eggshells in our picture having been drawn forward after hatching for the purpose of illustration. The second nest is in another hole in a tree, but this one is some fourteen feet high in an ash tree in a hedgerow. The third is typical of the rabbit-burrow site, the nest, in this case, being so far down the hole as to be completely out of sight and out of reach; and the last nest, in the ruined building, is situated on top of the substantial stone wall and is well covered and hidden by the slates. Incidentally, this plate shews the type of "hide" we use for such a situation; a framework of poles supporting a platform at the required level, and a screen of hessian around it to conceal us from the birds. They do not mind such a structure so long as it is erected gradually, a little at a time, and so long as it does not blow about or move in any way.

The usual clutch of the little owl consists of three, four, or five eggs, which are dull white, and remarkably broad for their length; in fact, they are very nearly spherical. They are generally laid in the early part of May and hatch in early June, so that it is during this latter month, when the parent little owls are feeding their young that we have the greatest opportunity to watch them closely and to photograph them.

The little owl is readily distinguished from the other British owls by its smaller size, its length of nine inches being less than two-thirds that of the tawny owl. It is frequently seen about by day, its flight being usually fairly direct and purposeful from tree to tree or from tree to ground, but characterised by a slight undulating tendency not unlike that of the woodpeckers. It perches freely on branches of trees, posts, and fences, and is often seen on the ground, where it runs about with remarkable agility. One bird that we were watching in Central Wales was seen several times to make a tour of the ant-hills in the vicinity, flying the longer distances from one to the next, but running the shorter gaps. It pecked vigorously at many of the hillocks as if it were finding something there, though we were not able, of course, to see what food it was collecting.

The plumage of the little owl is, on the whole, a cold brown colour, but, as may be seen in several of our photographs, the bird is liberally flecked with whitish markings. When seen at close quarters the little owl has a peculiar and character-istic expression as a result of a low forehead and a rather flat-topped skull. It has been well described as "frowning," and this, in conjunction with the keen-looking eyes, gives the bird a fierce and wicked appearance that may well have helped it to earn the bad reputation it gained as a new-comer to our fields.

As the little owl spread across the country, so did stories about its evil ways. It was accused of living chiefly on game chicks and song birds until there was a widespread clamour from landowners and gamekeepers for its extermination. This was in direct contradiction to its good record from abroad, and conflicted with the opinion of many people over here, so the British Trust for Ornithology embarked on a large-scale investigation to determine the facts. The enquiry lasted about eighteen months, including two breeding seasons, and the report* shows conclusively that, in general, the food of the little owl in this country is the same as on the Continent, and the bird is of great service in destroying agricultural pests.

In an earlier book†, we described how we set out to illustrate the feeding habits of the little owl during the breeding season, and how, in the course of taking numerous flashlight photographs, we recorded many cockchafer beetles

* Report of the Little Owl Food Enquiry 1936-37 by A. Hibbert-Ware (Witherby).
† Intimate Sketches from Bird Life (*Country Life*, 1940).

[*Continued on page* 46.

Plate 26.—Little owl with violet ground beetle (*flashlight*).

44

Plate 27.—Little owl with dor beetle
(*flashlight*).

45

Plate 28.—Little owl with cockchafer at entrance to nesting hole in a rabbit-burrow (*flashlight*).

and other invertebrates brought to the nest. We have been able to make numerous other observations since then and they confirm precisely what we wrote before. We have, in addition, seen one pair of little owls whose diet consisted very largely of earthworms and we were able to watch them tackle these exactly in the manner of a thrush—tugging at one end and leaning right back in their efforts to draw the worms from the earth. Another interesting incident we had the good fortune to observe, and have not recorded previously, was a short courtship display between two little owls. It was one evening in the middle of May, about an hour before sunset, when we heard a little owl begin to call from the roof of an old ruined shed. The note was "kee-wick", repeated several times; a clear, arresting

46

note that broke sharply into the evening stillness. We stood and listened, and almost at once we heard another answering call from a nearby ash tree, The answer was louder, more strident, and more rapidly repeated, and it was not long before we located the bird that made it—another little owl, perched among the branches. For some minutes the birds called to one another, sometimes loudly and excitedly, and at other times quite softly; and occasionally the bird on the roof would snap its bill sharply to make a resounding "click." Suddenly the bird in the tree left its perch, and flew round the roof of the shed, calling rapidly "pee-ou, pee-ou, pee-ou." He, for it was, as we afterwards discovered, the cock, alighted on the roof about a yard from the hen, and the two birds engaged in a duet of calls, becoming more and more excited as the cock gradually sidled towards her. When he was quite close, the hen began to droop and quiver her wings, and finally she crouched into a horizontal posture and mating took place. Such a display is fascinating to witness, yet it is surprisingly rarely seen. There is, indeed, still a lot to be recorded concerning the lives of the owls.

We mentioned earlier that the little owl seems to prefer country with a few

Plate 29.—Eggshells at entrance to little owl's nest.

Plate 30.—Little owl nesting site and hide.

trees about it. Indeed, in the case of every pair that we have watched, whatever the situation of the nest, it has been within a few yards of a tree that served as a favourite perch for the owls. For instance, at one nest, one of the birds, presumably the cock, could be seen roosting on a projecting bough during the day, and, regularly during the evening, it used it as a vantage point from which to drop on to its prey on the ground below. We used to watch it sitting there, for minutes on end. It might almost have been asleep except for the occasional slight move of the head that indicated it was, in reality, scrutinising the herbage below for any sign of movement. Suddenly it would dive down to the ground, catch something, and return at once to the perch, from which, after a few moments' hesitation, it would take the food to the nest.

48

The little owl does not always hunt from a perch, although, according to our observations, that is the most common method; neither does it necessarily take its prey on the ground. We recall seeing one little owl hover a few feet above a Norfolk marsh. Its fast-beating wings reminded us of a kestrel, and it dropped to the ground much in the manner of that bird. We have also seen the little owl quartering the ground as we shall presently describe in dealing with the short-eared owl; and, on several occasions we have observed the little owl hawking moths in the manner of the spotted flycatcher. The owl would fly out from the usual perch and take the moth by a short upward flight, after which it would return again to the perch to look for further victims.

Since we made our first photographic records of the little owl bringing food to the nest, a number of other bird photographers have done similar work and, since their pictures were obtained in different parts of the country, it is of interest to compare their results with ours. Thus we find that Mr. T. M. Fowler, the president of the Zoological Photographic Club, working at a nest in Yorkshire, has records

[*Continued on page* 52.

Plate 31.—Little owl emerging from nesting hole (*flashlight*).

Plate 32.—Little o
with cockcha
beetle at entra
to nesting hole
(*flashlig*

Plate 33.—Anc
cockchafer b
is brought to
nest (*flashligh*

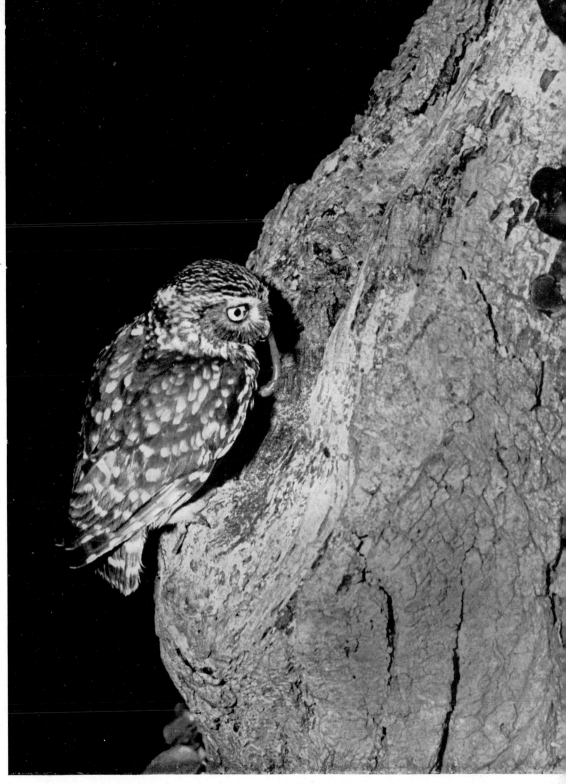

Plate 34.—The nest on this occasion was in the hole of an ash-tree (*flashlight*).

of thirteen beetles, one caterpillar, one snail, and one mouse; while Captain G. K. Yeates, writing of little owls that he has watched from a hide in Dorset, says, "insects and earthworms have formed exclusively the food of the chicks, at least while I have been in my hides." He also reports, however, having once "found a little owl sitting in a regular feather bed of dead starlings and song-thrushes." Another photographer, Mr. F. G. Phillips, working in Berkshire, found a similiar diet, which he summed up as "beetles, moths, etc., and occasional small birds."

In the course of his watching, Mr. Phillips witnessed an unusual incident which illustrates the courage of the little owl. The young owls were five weeks old at the time and, being able to fly a little, were in the habit of leaving their nest in a hollow tree and flying on to the top of his hide. They were up in this position one night when a large rat climbed the tree and entered the nesting hole. It soon looked out again, and, as it did so, one of the young owls flew down and attacked it. The young owl and the rat were locked together in a fierce fight, when one of the parent little owls arrived back. It flew straight in to the attack and the fight went on, mostly inside the hole. After about two minutes the noise died down and the old bird left, and when, some time later, Mr. Phillips shone a torch into the hole, he found the rat there, dead, and covered with blood.

It is interesting to note that, besides being introduced to this country, the little owl was also introduced into New Zealand, in 1906, and that a very similar situation arose there. The little owl was accused of being a menace to the native birds. There, too, a study* was made of the bird's feeding habits, and it was found that, as in other parts of the world, the little owl's diet is almost entirely insect-tivorous. There are minor variations resulting from the different conditions from one place to another, but they are almost negligible. For example, in New Zealand, caterpillars head the list of insects, and they, beetles, and earwigs, be-tween them, account for the vast majority of the little owl's food. As in Europe a few small birds appear in the list, but it is significant that none of New Zealand's native birds is included.

Thus, taking into consideration all the work that has been done to determine the food of the little owl, and in this we are not unmindful of several reports from reliable observers of the little owl's depredations among certain song birds, we are forced to the conclusion that the little owl is not, in general, the rogue he is so often made out to be. There are, undoubtedly, a few special cases where, owing to abnormal conditions, the little owl cannot be tolerated, but, by and large, it is a most useful bird in the countryside and should be allowed to go its way without undue interference by man.

* B. J. Marples—A study of the little owl in New Zealand.
Trans. Roy. Soc. of N.Z. Vol. 72 part of 3 pp. 237-252. Dec., 1942.

The Long-Eared Owl

THE MORE we saw of the owls, the more fascinating we found them, but we always looked forward particularly to opportunities of watching the long-eared owl for this is, in our opinion, the most nocturnal of them all. It is very seldom to be seen about in daylight unless it is disturbed from its nest or roosting-place, and only little has been published about the activities of this bird, probably because of the extreme difficulty of making observations in the dark.

The long-eared owl is predominantly a tree-haunting species, spending the greater part of its time in copses and plantations, especially of conifers, and, where suitable habitats occur, is to be found in most parts of the British Isles except the Shetlands and the Outer Hebrides. Its numbers vary greatly, however, from place to place, and whereas in some places, especially in Wales, it is very sparsely distributed, yet in others, particularly in Ireland, it is the commonest owl. Abroad, it is to be found over the greater part of Europe; in western Asia; and across Siberia to Japan; while a closely allied race inhabits the temperate parts of North America.

The appearance of the long-eared owl in the field varies a great deal, depending on how and where the bird is seen. If, by chance, we come upon it during the day, we shall probably find it a tall, slim figure, perched on a projecting stump or branch of a tree, with its body pressed close to the trunk. It is really smaller than the tawny owl, but often appears taller on account of the prominent erect ear-tufts which give the bird its name. We should perhaps remark that these tufts are not really ears; they are merely elongated feathers. The ears, as in all other birds, are hidden under the feathers at the sides of the head. In flight the ear-tufts are often depressed and not visible, but the bird may be distinguished from the short-eared owl by its much greyer general colouring, and by its shorter and broader wings.

The plumage of the long-eared owl is beautifully marked with bars and flecks of buff, grey, and brown on the upper parts ; and the breast and underparts are a stone colour, boldly streaked with brown. The facial disk is well defined. It is buff with a dark edging and with a very conspicuous V-marking between and above the eyes. The iris of the eye is a bright golden-orange colour, but we need to be quite close to see this.

Such, briefly, is the bird we set out to watch early one April. A friend living in the northern part of Norfolk—that delightful stretch of undulating wooded heathland lying east of the Wash—had found a nest, and had invited us to stay with him to keep it under observation, and we had lost no time in joining him and visiting the site.

We made our way along a by-road traversing a sandy tract that was over-grown with birch scrub and heather, and presently turned off towards a small

Plate 35.—Long-eared owl nesting habitat in Norfolk.

wood on our right. We entered this and found it to be a plantation of Scots pine intermingled with a few spruce firs, about thirty to forty feet high. They were well spaced, with very little undergrowth, and we could see a fair way through the wood. We followed our guide until we came near a particular spruce, and there, in a crutch some twenty-three feet up, was a bulky nest. A head, surmounted by two horn-like growths, peered over the rim and down at us, and we knew that the long-eared owl was brooding. The nest we describe is typical of the long-eared owl, though various other situations may be used. Sometimes the bird prefers an old squirrel's drey or a magpie's nest, and in some localities it nests on the ground. In such a case the nest is often in the shelter of undergrowth in a wood. There can be little doubt though, that the long-eared owl prefers to be

54

off the ground if possible, and one year we made an experiment to verify this. Early in January, we built an imitation "crow's nest" in a copse in which a pair of long-eared owls nested regularly, but in which, because of the incidence of winter gales, there were no natural tree nests to serve them. Sure enough the long-eared owls used our "nest" that year and forsook their accustomed position on the ground.

Apart from these sites, we have noticed in certain woods of ancient oaks where decay has led to the formation of large hollow shells in the upper parts of the boles, the saucer-shaped bottoms of these hollows are favourite nesting sites for the long-eared owls. They are used almost to the exclusion of all other situations in these particular localities.

Our friend had begun building a hide, so we pushed ahead with the construction of this as fast as seemed prudent, and had it completed and ready for use within a few days.

As we climbed to the hide for our first spell of close-up observation, the owl

[*Continued on page* 58.

Plate 36.—Nest of long-eared owl on the ground.

Plate 37.—Hiding-place erected for photographing long-eared owls nesting in a tree.

Plate 38.—Long-eared owl and nest (*daylight*).

sat tight until we were half-way up the ladder, and then left silently and flew out of sight. We suspected, however, that she did not go out of the wood, so we quickly installed ourselves and settled down to our vigil.

It was 10.30 a.m. and a fine and fairly bright day. We peered out from the peep-hole in the front of the hide and there, seven feet in front of us, was the nest with its clutch of five white eggs. It was a shallow bowl made of pine twigs, and appeared to be an old nest of a carrion crow. There was no lining, except for a few pieces of dead bracken and a few feathers which had probably been rubbed from the breast of the sitting bird.

Within a very short time, we noticed the long-eared owl cautiously making her way back to the nest. She alighted on a pine tree a little way off and stood there, bowing up and down. From a crouched position, in which her head was almost on a level with the branch on which she was perched, she would straighten up to her full height and sway sideways. After a few moments she would stoop again and repeat the performance, and all the time her eyes were fixed steadily in our direction and she appeared to be staring right through us. She gradually made her way towards the nest, jumping or flying from tree to tree and from branch to branch until, reaching the perch just above and behind the nest, she paused momentarily as if to see that all was well.

Soon she shuffled forward and worked her way on to the eggs, and as she did so we were able to get a photograph (plate 41) which shews her aggressive display, occasioned, no doubt, by the, as yet, unfamiliar presence of the camera lens. It will be noticed that the facial disk is drawn fully forward and that the feathers fairly bristle. The ear tufts are fully erect on this occasion, as indeed they are in all the other photographs which shew aggressive display during daylight. It is of interest to observe, however, that aggressive display after dark is characterized by the same extension of the facial disk, but that, on all such occasions that we have recorded, the ear-tufts have been depressed, rather than erect.

The owl soon settled down to brood the eggs and remained in one attitude, practically motionless, for some hours. There was nothing particular to note during the rest of our watch, except that, when the bird relaxed, as she soon did, the face assumed a rather pinched appearance and became almost cat-like (plate 42). This appears to be the more normal expression for the long-eared owl. On another occasion when we were watching the long-eared owl by day there was the same lack of activity. The brooding hen changed her position only twice in the course of eight hours and the cock was not seen or heard at all. He became active, however, towards dusk, and most evenings he could be heard calling softly from a perch somewhere near the nest. Sometimes the hen would answer him and a brief "conversation" would ensue.

One evening, it was April 28th, just as it was getting dark in the wood, we

[Continued on page 60.

Plates *39 and 40*.—Long-eared owl playing peep-bo behind trunk of tree (*flashlight*).

Plate 41.—Aggressive attitude of a long-eared owl (*daylight*).

had a brief glimpse of a nuptial display. The hen, as we could tell from her call, was perched on a tree a short distance from the nest, but, unfortunately, not in view of the hide. The cock answered and flew towards her. We had brief glimpses of him as he flew between the trees, dipping and rising, and occasionally making a "clapping" sound with his wings. He circled round and round the spot where we knew the hen to be, and finally alighted somewhere close to her. He had not called while in flight, but he now began a low moaning note. This did not last long. The hen came back to the nest to resume brooding and the wood became quiet again except for the "cooing" of numerous roosting pigeons.

Plate 42.—Normal attitude while brooding (*daylight*).

When we visited the nest early on the morning of May 2nd, we found that the first egg had just hatched and the chick was still wet. It was covered in soft white down, slightly tinted by the pink skin underneath, which shewed through faintly. As it lay there among the four remaining eggs, it squeaked weakly and kicked as if to exercise its legs. It appeared very frail, and its eyes, like those of the other owls, did not open for the first few days; but it shewed, nevertheless, distinct owl characteristics and even had two small protuberances on the top of the head corresponding to the ear-tufts in the adult birds.

It is of interest to note that, on this same morning when the first chick was found hatched, we found food on the side of the nest for the first time. It consisted of two short-tailed field-voles and one rat, all of which had been decapitated. Did the cock know by some means that the chicks had been hatched, or did he bring the food to his sitting mate because, at this critical period, she refused to leave the nest, even for the short period required for feeding? We watched from the hide for the whole of that morning but did not see any of this food used, either for the chick or by the hen herself. She merely remained quietly brooding during the whole time we were there.

A further egg hatched during the afternoon, and we resolved to spend the whole night in the hide. As we made our way towards the wood a little before dusk, a nightingale was singing vigorously from a tangle of bushes just by our path. We paused for a few moments to listen to his clear, ringing notes, and he, ignoring our presence, continued to pour forth his melody within a few feet of where we stood. The song of the nightingale seems to have extraordinary carry-ing power when heard against the evening stillness, and as we resumed our way to the long-eared owl, the voice of Philomel went with us into the wood.

Darkness fell quickly in the wood, and by 9.45 p.m. we could barely see the nest in front of us. Black, indefinite shapes were all that remained of the nearby trees, and the eerie silence was made even more weird by the occasional rustle as some little creature made its way among the dead twigs and pieces on the ground beneath us. Time seemed to pass very slowly as we sat there tensely expecting something to happen, when suddenly, from a little way off, the cock long-eared owl called a long-drawn-out "ooo-o-o." He was answered at once from the nest by the brooding hen. Her note almost defies description but can perhaps be likened to the noise made by drawing air through a comb covered with tissue paper. As far as we could tell, the cock did not come to the nest during the early part of the night, but the two birds kept up an exchange of calls about every ten to fifteen minutes.

About 1.10 a.m. the cock called loudly from very close to the nest—a blood-curdling note it was at that time in the morning in the darkness and loneliness of the wood—and a few minutes later there was a slight rustle on the branches beyond the nest. Judging by the noises of apparent excitement, we felt sure that the cock had brought in some food to his mate, but the night was, unfortunately, much too dark for us to see anything. Whatever took place was short, however, for after a few seconds all became quiet again and we heard nothing more until the cock resumed his intermittent calling from a little way off. His next visit was shortly after 3 a.m. It was as brief as before and the night was still too dark for us to see what took place, but about half an hour later the approach of dawn enabled us to make out the shadowy outline of the nest and we hoped for a further visit so that we could have a glimpse of the owls' behaviour. After a preliminary exchange of calls with the brooding hen, the cock came in to the nest again at 3.45 a.m. and though we could just discern his movements we were still unable

62

[Continued on page 64.

Plate 43.—The male long-eared owl brings a young rat to the nest. The hen is brooding newly hatched chicks (*flashlight*).

to see whether he carried any food. Presently, however, when the light had increased, we saw that there were two fresh rats on the nest, and as the hen had not been away at all during the night it is certain that the cock brought in food on at least two of his visits. It seems probable that he did so on each occasion and that some of the food was eaten during the hours of darkness.

At about 4.30 a.m. the hen left the nest, possibly for a little exercise. She appeared to join her mate, for we heard something of a "conversation" taking place, but she clearly felt a strong urge to return to the nest, and she was back after an absence of only eighteen minutes. She settled to brood and relapsed into silence, as did the cock, with the approach of day, and we, sensing the onset of a period of inactivity and feeling somewhat cramped and sleepy, left the hide at 5.30 a.m.

We resumed our vigil the next evening and found that a third chick had hatched during the day. As before, the hen long-eared owl was back within a few minutes of our entry into the hide, and, settling over the chicks, tucked them under her. Their high-pitched squeaky voices faded away as she did so, and all was quiet for a while.

Events, generally, were similar to those of the previous night, except that, from time to time, the chicks were more active and their excited squeaking led us to suppose that they were being fed. They seemed to have four feeds during the night, the last one just after 4 a.m. when we could dimly see what was taking place. The hen was tearing at the prey and passing it under her to the chicks. She did not stand to one side to feed them as do most of the birds of prey. This meal lasted for twelve minutes.

It was fairly light when, at 4.50 a.m., we had a great thrill. The cock had been calling for some minutes without getting any reply from the hen, when he suddenly arrived behind the nest with a young rat dangling from his bill. He was in a state of considerable emotional excitement and was flapping his wings and clutching and unclutch'ng at the branch on which he stood, so giving his body a kind of rolling motion. The hen, too, was very excited, and with quivering wings and a chirruping call she reached up to the cock and took the food from him.

Things became quiet again after this and the hen continued brooding until we disturbed her when leaving the hide at breakfast time. We noticed when she had gone that the fourth chick had hatched during the night, leaving only one egg in the nest. This fifth chick hatched during that day, only about forty-eight hours after the first one. Such a happening is unusual among the owls and, indeed, among most of the birds of prey. They usually start incubation as soon as the first egg is laid and continue laying at about two-day intervals, so that the chicks hatch out at similar intervals and the oldest is some eight or ten days in

64

[*Continued on page* 69.

Plate 44.—The hen long-eared owl appears to admire her young (*daylight*).

Plate 45.—The hen goes to fetch her own food, and returns with the remains of a fully-grown rat—on the left of the nest may be seen a long-tailed field-mouse (*flashlight*).

66

Plate 46.—The newly hatched long-eared owlets take shelter under their mother during meal-times. The prey—a rat—can be seen just in front of the hen (*flashlight*).

Plate 47.—Young long-eared owl (*daylight*).

advance of the youngest. In the present case it would appear that incubation did not begin until the fourth egg was laid, or possibly not until the clutch was complete.

Our next spell in the hide was by daylight. It was a fine, warm afternoon, with the sun shining brilliantly. We noticed that the elder chicks had now grown a thicker covering of down and had lost all the pink tinge they had at first. They were pure white with the facial disks beginning to shew. As usual, the hen came back almost as soon as we were installed. She settled to brood all five chicks, and remained thus for the whole of the three hours we spent in the hide on this occasion. The heat worried her a good deal, and we noticed, particularly during the early part of the afternoon, that she panted heavily, with her bill slightly open, and vibrated her throat rapidly.

We returned to our lodgings for an evening meal and resumed the vigil in the hide shortly after dark. It was a lovely night, with not a breath of wind, and the occasional sounds of the wood broke sharply into the stilly silence. An occasional peewit could be heard and a stone-curlew flying across the neighbouring heath; and every now and then the nightingale broke in with his rich, fluty warbles and trills.

The hen brooded quietly for the first part of the night and no sound was heard from the cock until about 12.20 a.m. He then called and, two minutes later, came down to the nest. The two birds engaged in what sounded like a "conversation" for about half a minute, after which the cock flew away. Again the night was intensely dark and we could not see what was happening, but after a few minutes we heard a good deal of activity accompanied by whistling noises from the chicks, and, judging by other meals that we had seen, we concluded that the chicks were now being fed. The meal lasted just over half an hour and was followed by another period of quiet until 3.25 a.m. when the hen left the nest. She was away for 16 minutes and when she came back it was just light enough for us to see that she carried something in her bill; we subsequently identified this as a full-grown rat; an interesting capture, we thought, since all the other rats we had seen at this nest were young of various sizes. This was the only occasion on which we saw the hen actually bring food to the nest, and even this food, we believe, was originally caught by the cock. Just before the hen's return we heard the two birds exchanging calls, and a moment later there was a light thud on the ground, followed by a rustling of leaves. Our interpretation was that the cock accidentally dropped the rat as he was passing it to the hen and that she had flown down to the ground and retrieved it.

No food was given to the chicks at this time and all remained quiet until about 4.30 a.m. when the cock came to the nest after exchanging calls with the hen. There was the same excited wing quivering as before while he passed her the food he had brought, but it was remarkable that, in spite of the obvious attachment

69

of these two birds, the cock should spend so little time at or near the nest. He left as soon as the hen had accepted the food from him.

At 4.41 a.m. the chicks were fed again. It was by now quite light and we could see how the hen held the prey under her right talon and pulled upwards with her bill to tear off pieces of meat. At first there was a considerable amount of fur attached and these portions she swallowed herself, gulping them down with her head thrown well back; but presently, when she came to the meat, it was passed down, a small piece at a time, to the chicks, who remained practically hidden under her body and wings. When the chicks were satisfied, the hen swallowed the remainder of the prey herself, and picked around at the nest to clean it of small pieces that had been dropped during the meal, but she did not touch a rat and a short-tailed field-vole that were lying on the side of the nest and were apparently intended for future consumption.

We spent several more days and nights with these owls and noted much the same general procedure as we have already described. During the first five days of the chicks' hatching, the following food was actually observed on the nest; 19 rats, 7 field-mice, and 2 field-voles. Other prey was no doubt brought in, but was eaten during darkness and was consequently not seen and recorded. Apart from this a number of pellets were analysed and these also revealed a diet consisting entirely of rodents. The long-eared owl would thus appear to be of considerable value to the farmer and mankind in general.

It was noticeable, possibly because these owls do not fly about much by day, that they were very little disturbed by the other birds that were quite numerous in the wood. Once in the evening, when the hen was returning to the nest after being disturbed by our entry into the hide, we saw her mobbed by a pair of jays, and on this occasion, the cock accompanied her and appeared to try and draw the jays' attention from the vicinity of the nest. He flew to a nearby spruce and perched close to the trunk. The jays followed and continued to mob him for a little while, but soon they lost interest and departed.

One thing that struck us, throughout our observations, was the facility with which these long-eared owls flew about among the tangle of pine branches by day and by night. Right through the darkest of nights the cock continued hunting successfully and came back without making even a rustle or a scratch until he touched down on the perch just behind the nest. Their eyesight is really amazing as will be better understood by reference to the concluding chapter.

Our stay in Norfolk came to an end before the young long-eared owls were ready to leave the nest, but our friend kept watch on them and advised us that all five chicks left the nest on May 25th. Their fledging period was thus twenty-one to twenty-three days.

Plate 48.—Newly fledged long-eared owls (*daylight*).

The Short-Eared Owl

I T WAS a fine, still, evening in the early part of May, 1933, when, in company
with the late Mr. Jim Vincent, then keeper of Lord Desborough's bird sanctuary
near Hickling in Norfolk, we set out to watch the marshes for signs of the short-
eared owl. Unlike the other British owls, the short-eared shuns the woodland
and is to be found in open country; on marshes, heaths and moorland. Its
greatest stronghold is undoubtedly the Orkneys and Outer Hebrides, but it is
nowhere common, and, south of the Mersey and Humber, it nests only irregularly
except in Norfolk, Suffolk, and Cambridgeshire, where a few pairs nest most
years; but it may be seen in other parts of the country during the winter, when
our short-eared owl population is considerably augmented by visitors from the
Continent.

We had found the short-eared to be the most elusive of the British-breeding
owls, and as we made our way along the dusty Norfolk lanes between hedges
fresh with the young green of hawthorn and wild rose, we were talking over the
prospects of seeing this bird in its breeding haunts. There had been, it appeared,
several short-eared owls hunting these marshes during the winter, but little had
been seen of them for some weeks and it was uncertain whether any had stayed
to nest. We passed beyond the lane and our way was now a mere track alongside
a row of bushes that stood out as a promontory into the edge of the marsh.

Redshank and peewits flew to and fro, and snipe drummed intermittently in
the distance, while, nearer at hand, yellow wagtails flitted about and ran nimbly
through the herbage, their bright yellow breasts seeming to be tinged with gold
as they caught and reflected the evening glow. After a little while of revelling in
this delightful scene, our attention was directed by Jim Vincent to a speck he had
noticed moving low across the marsh, more than a mile away. We could not at
first pick it out, even under his direction, but his practised eye had seen it unaided
and had recognised the characteristic flight of the short-eared owl.

Gradually the bird worked its way toward us, and we began to appreciate its
easy, buoyant, and unhurried wing action. The slow, regular rhythm was interrupted every now and then by a wheeling glide on outstretched wings, and we
could not help feeling that here was one of the most entrancing performers that
ever enjoyed the power of flight. Soon it was wheeling some fifty feet above us,
its blunt head turned downward as it scrutinised the ground below. Its great
expanse of wing was beautifully marked in various shades of fawn set off
by darker crescent markings near the tips, and as it turned and banked
close overhead, it revealed the golden sandy colour of the upper surface of
its wings.

The short-eared owl is somewhat nomadic, and, apart from the influx of
birds in winter, the numbers in any particular place vary considerably from time

to time according to the food supply. This owl lives very largely on small mammals, particularly the short-tailed field-vole, and it seems that the distribution of this rodent has a considerable influence on the distribution of the short-eared owl. For instance, it is a remarkable fact that, although both these creatures have a very wide range over the surface of the earth, their areas coincide very closely, and the owl is not found in places from which the vole, or one of its near relatives is absent. Moreover, the vole, like many other creatures, is subject to recurrent periods of excessive breeding, and at such times the short-eared owls may congregate in large numbers in the districts affected by the vole plague, and help to keep the rodents in check. The voles are then piled high on and around the nest, the number caught being far in excess of the birds' requirements. At such times the short-eared owls become much more prolific than usual and, instead of the normal 4 or 5 eggs, may lay as many as 13 or 14, and have been known to rear this large family.

Since our first introduction to the short-eared owl, we have watched it, with varying success, during several breeding seasons. We had hoped to make the journey to the Orkneys, which is undoubtedly the best locality in the British Isles for this study, but, so far, circumstances have prevented this excursion and our observations have been confined to Norfolk, Suffolk and Yorkshire. The Norfolk birds, which have been our principal study, are to be found chiefly on the marshes between the Broads and the sea, and they have, in consequence, been to some extent affected by the disastrous floods which swept this region when the sea broke through the sandhills near Horsey in 1938. The sea water killed a large part of the flora and fauna of the district, including, no doubt, the majority of the field-voles, and possibly because of this, there has been a marked scarcity of short-eared owls since that time. They are beginning now to re-establish themselves in small numbers, but the process is slow and has been hampered by the very severe winters in 1939 and 1940. Thus, in 1941, we could not locate even one pair of short-eared owls nesting in the district. Occasional single birds were seen during May, but they were, in all probability, merely passing through on their way to other breeding haunts.

In 1942 we were more successful, but, in spite of considerable searching, only one nest was found in the locality. This was on May 11th, when it contained four eggs. As shewn in plate 51, the nest was a roughly constructed hollow among the coarse grass, but it is of interest because the short-eared is the only one of our owls that attempts any construction. The others merely use existing nests of other birds as in the case of the long-eared owl, or lay their eggs direct in the bottom of a hole without any attempt at lining it. The nest in this case was well sheltered under a tuft of tangled grasses, the site being on the open marsh only a few hundred yards inland from the sandhills that fringe the coast.

The circumstances of its discovery are rather remarkable. No one seemed to

73

know of its existence until, in the course of fighting a fire that was sweeping through the dried-up grass and herbage, a keeper noticed two short-eared owls flying in and out of the smoke and calling frantically as if very much distressed. He felt sure they must have a nest nearby and went across to the spot that was attracting the birds' attention. There he found the nest only a short distance ahead of the flames, so, with water from a dyke and by the skilful use of a fire-broom, he diverted the fire to pass round the nest, leaving an island of vegetation in the midst of the burnt and blackened marsh-land.

When we saw what had happened we were afraid that the owls would forsake the place altogether, but, fortunately, our fears proved to be unfounded, and the following evening we found the hen sitting tightly on her eggs. So tightly did she sit, in fact, that we were able to approach to within a few feet without disturbing her. The cock, however, shewed his displeasure by flying close overhead and diving at us repeatedly. He was very aggressive, but his actions gave us an excellent opportunity to notice his graceful and effortless flight, and we were able to take a number of photographs which shew the beauty of his wings. Their span of nearly three feet is extraordinary for the size of the bird.

Several evenings after this we saw the short-eared owl hunting across the marsh, but we did not visit the nest again until we heard from the keeper that the eggs were hatching. This was on the 21st May and, when we went to the site that evening, we found two chicks about a day old in the nest with the remaining two eggs. The cock was still very bold in defence of the nest, stooping at us with half-folded wings and calling at us with a very gruff note.

We kept this nest under observation for some time, both by day and after dark, and we observed that, although it was not unusual to see the cock bird about during daylight, these short-eared owls were predominantly crepuscular. The cock seldom appeared to be hunting during his daylight excursions, and even when he was, there was none of the methodical quartering of the ground which is such a feature of these birds in the evening; and during the whole of our observations we never saw the cock bring food to the hen during the morning or afternoon. She, for her part, was comparatively inactive by day; brooding the eggs, and subsequently the young chicks; and later, when they no longer needed brooding, she would roost somewhere, probably on the ground in a secluded spot from which she never seemed to be disturbed.

By the middle of the evening, however, a marked change came over the owls. The hen, sitting on the nest, was much more alert than she had been during the day. Then, she had been comparatively oblivious of small noises, but now, the least sound caused her to turn and glare savagely. The cock usually began hunting in earnest about half-past seven (double summer time). He just appeared as from nowhere, and from then onwards could be seen most of the time working to and fro across the marsh, his buoyant wings beating steadily, with a pause

74 [*Continued on page* 76.

Plate 49.—Short-eared owl perched on the top of a dead tree (*daylight*).

every now and then while he swept onwards in an easy glide. From time to time he would hesitate, swing upwards and back a yard or two, and perhaps hover momentarily over some spot where he suspected a rodent in the herbage. Often he would be mistaken, and, after a second glance at the ground, would resume his flight; but sometimes, his suspicions confirmed by the second look, he would drop rapidly to the ground to seize the object of his attention. We noticed that he usually swallowed the first one or two catches himself, and then, having taken the edge off his own appetite, he turned his attention to the family.

Hunting went on throughout the evening, though food was brought to the nest only a few times, and at irregular intervals. Until the chicks were about a week old, they needed brooding for the greater part of the time and, in consequence, the hunting was almost entirely the cock's responsibility; but thereafter the hen would leave the chicks for increasing periods and would do a certain amount of hunting on her own.

As so often happens to creatures of the wild, these owls were not, alas, to live their normal course without accident, and, when the chicks were about eight days old, the cock was shot by some troops stationed in the neighbourhood. This, of course, put an extra strain on the hen, and as she, too, was shot at several times, though, fortunately, without harm, her behaviour was, to some extent, unnatural, and we shall, therefore, omit a detailed description of her life at the nest, and pass on to a pair we watched the following year.

As the effects of the salt water flooding in the Hickling area slowly diminished, so the short-eared owls gradually re-established themselves, and in 1943 we found evidence of three pairs, though only two of the nesting sites were actually discovered, as the third was within an area fenced off by the military authorities. The one that we shall describe was situated under a large clump of common rush which screened it well from behind and above. Again, in this case, there was a definite attempt at nest construction, pieces of rush being broken into short lengths and arranged to form a saucer-shaped mattress, on which the eggs were laid.

The nest was found on May 18th, when there were three eggs, one of which was on the point of hatching. Two days later we erected a hide about forty feet from the nest so that the owls should have a chance to get used to it from a distance.

The following evening we moved the hide much closer to the nest and achieved this without disturbing the hen. She crouched low on the nest and glared at us with her facial disk thrust well forward. Her aggressive display was enhanced by the way she lifted her wings a little and raised the feathers on her back, but, though we really took note of all this, we appeared to ignore her, and, having completed our task, we left her still brooding.

Two days passed before we visited the owls again, and this time we moved our hide right up into position for photography—eight feet from the nest. The hen

Plate 50.—Field-vole—the principal food of the short-eared owl.

left during this operation and we noticed that all three chicks were now hatched.

Our first spell of detailed observation from this hide was in the morning after we had completed our preparations. It was just after nine o'clock when we approached the short-eared owl. She must have been brooding the young chicks at the time, for we saw her leave the nest as we drew near. She flew well away and alighted first on a dead stump of a tree, and then, after a short pause, flew down to an earthy mound where she stood looking about her. We watched her for a few moments and then, after a brief inspection of the nest (there was still no food in store), we quickly settled ourselves

77

Plate 51.—Short-eared owl's nest and eggs.

into the hide. We looked out through the peep-hole at the young chicks. They were so huddled together that it was difficult to make out how many they were, even though we knew there to be three. They seemed just one mass of greyish-white down. The nest made a pleasing picture with the canopy of drooping rush and we hoped more than ever that this bird would be a good "sitter." We were not disappointed and soon she alighted in the rush a few feet behind the nest and cautiously made her way forward, stopping every now and then to peer over the herbage at the hide. It was intensely exciting to watch her approach and to see her walk on to the nest, tuck the young under her, and begin to brood them.

Having now an opportunity to study this bird closely for the first time, we

Plate 52.—The short-eared owl brooding (*daylight*).

were struck by the beauty of the plumage. Her general colouring was rather lighter than that of the other short-eared owls we had watched, and the brownish feathers on her back and wings seemed to be tinged with gold. Her buff-coloured facial disk was edged with a distinct light-grey rim and her golden-yellow fascinating eyes were set in small disks of black feathers. She was certainly one of the most handsome birds we had been privileged to watch, but we noted as well, alas, that she was also decidedly nervous. Low-flying aircraft upset her considerably, and, as they passed over, she gazed upwards with her ear-tufts raised and her facial disk drawn back—not aggressive, this time, but seemingly rather anxious. Small noises in the hide disturbed her, and consequently, as she sat there brooding

79

those young chicks only four, three, and two, days old, we kept as quiet as we possibly could and refrained from taking any photographs.

Our restraint was justified, and gradually the owl became reconciled to the inevitable slight noises we made. The next day she came back to the nest without hesitation, and we felt that we could begin photography. As she first stood over the young, she turned and glared at the hide and looked searchingly in all directions until she was sure that all was well, but then, having satisfied herself, she settled down to brood. Each chick in turn was guided into position with the mother's bill, and then when they were all comfortable, she fluffed out her breast feathers and lowered herself over them.

The hen gradually relaxed and seemed to doze, but we noticed that she retained the ability to rouse almost instantly to a state of vigilance at the slightest provocation. For instance, she appeared to be asleep when a Montagu's harrier flew by not far from the nest. We saw it approach but did not hear any sound to mark its passage, yet the short-eared owl became aware of its presence and woke immediately to assume an attitude of defiance. From time to time the chicks became restive and disturbed the hen. One or other of them would push out from under her breast and rub its head among her feathers, "chittering" as it did so, and she in turn would look down at it as in admiration and would occasionally utter a soft note in reply.

After about an hour and a half of brooding, the hen began to preen herself. Using her bill, she carefully combed the feathers along her back; then her wings, working from the undersides; and finally her breast. She paid particular attention here and there to certain feathers as if they may have been specially soiled, and took about twenty minutes to complete her toilet.

Following this the hen brooded for the greater part of the time and was disturbed only by the fidgeting of the chicks. She would sometimes lift a wing or raise her whole body to allow one of them to move its position; to wriggle further under her; or to come out for an airing; and it was of interest to note that even at this early age the chicks would push themselves out backwards from under her and defecate over the rim of the nest, though very little excrement was actually passed at this period. During a spell in the hide the following morning, we noticed that, on her return to the nest, the hen picked the dry excrement from the surrounding rush and swallowed it. Was this done, we wondered, because the white litter was becoming too conspicuous.

The largest chick was by now six days old, and was beginning to shew the first signs of feathering, and we noted, too, that all the chicks still had the egg-tooth—that remarkable little horny growth on the upper mandible, used for rubbing and eventually chipping the eggshell at the time of hatching. There was still no food to be seen on the nest and we had not, up to now, in the course of these daylight observations, seen any food caught or offered to the chicks. It was,

80

[Continued on page 82.

Plate 53.   *Plate 54.*

Short-eared owl in flight.

Plate 55.   *Plate 56.*

Plate 57.—The enormous stretch of wings of the short-eared owl (*daylight*).

then, with considerable eagerness that we began our first twilight vigil that evening.

We arrived rather later than we had intended and it was 9 p.m. before we were settled in the hide. The chicks had, it seemed, been fed quite recently, for there were fresh meadow-pipit feathers about the nest, and one chick still had pieces of food protruding from its bill. All of them were very sleepy and, when the hen returned, she quickly settled down to brood them. Presently she began to call softly "wherr-ack," lifting her head as she did so, as if calling to her mate. The call was repeated several times at intervals of a few seconds, and then, after a lull of a minute or more, was taken up again. The cock, however, must have been hunting some distance off, for he did not answer, neither did we see anything of him ; and he must have been finding food difficult to catch that evening, for although the chicks were obviously hungry, he had not put in an appearance when we left the hide at 11.30 p.m.

Resolved to be in time for the first feed next evening, we set out for the hide at six o'clock. Though the young owls were now seven, six, and five days old, the hen was still brooding them very closely, and did not leave until we were within a couple of yards of her. As was her custom, she flew away without any attempt to mob us, and alighted on a mound some 200 yards from the nest. From there she flew to a favourite stump and preened herself for a short while before starting to hunt. She quartered the ground only a few feet above the herbage, dropping occasionally when something caught her eye, but failing, as far as we could see, to make a catch; and presently she returned to the stump. Here, after a little while, she was attacked by a cock Montagu's harrier which dived at her several times. It did not actually make contact, but flew close enough to make the owl duck her head and call out at each attack. As is usual in such fights between birds, the attacker soon tired of the sport and went back to his business of hunting across the marsh. In the course of hunting, however, he chanced to make his way towards the position of the short-eared owl's nest, and the owl, sensing danger, left her perch and flew straight at him. It was now his turn to dodge. He turned and twisted and side-slipped to avoid her sallies, and soon beat a hasty retreat from the marsh. The owl, satisfied at his departure, returned to her stump, but no sooner was she settled than she became the victim of a mobbing attack by swallows. They flew round, swooping and diving close by her, and again she had to duck her head in defence, but again the attackers soon passed to other diversions and the owl was left in peace.

It was 7.50 p.m. when the short-eared owl eventually returned to her nest. Her first action was to pick up and swallow two pellets which she had cast up and left on the rim of the nest sometime previously, and then she went on to pick at sundry small pieces of excrement which were fouling the surrounding grasses. Having tidied the place to her satisfaction, she settled to brood her chicks, and no sooner had she done so than she began to call just as she did the previous evening. This time, however, there was a reply, and very soon, like a bolt from the blue and with a rapid beating of wings, the cock alighted in front of the nest, carrying a field-vole in his bill. Never before or since have we seen such agitation and excitement as then ensued. The hen was mewing rapidly and quivering her wings and every feather on her body seemed fluffed out and tremulous. So large did she seem to become that her face with its glaring but lovely eyes seemed to be the centre of a great mass of quivering feathers. The cock, too, was excited in the presence of his mate. He stepped across to her, his wings flapping violently and his feathers shivering vigorously, and passed her the vole; and no sooner had he done so than he sprang into the air and was gone. The whole episode was so short and the birds' excitement had so gripped us that we failed to make a photographic record of the event.

The young owls obviously suspected that a meal was imminent for they began to call out more excitedly than we had ever heard them before; and they were not to be disappointed. The hen seized the vole under the talons of one foot, and, with a single powerful wrench, tore off the head. She swallowed this herself, presumably because the skull would have been too large for the chicks to manage, but, directly afterwards, she began to pull off pieces of meat from the body of the vole and these, though they had a good deal of fur still attached to them, were fed to the chicks. The greatest part of the food seemed to go to one chick, the largest one, but in spite of this he was still ravenous, and, when half the vole had been consumed, he grabbed the remainder from the hen and swallowed it, including the hind legs, without difficulty. The whole meal had lasted less than two minutes.

The hen now tucked the chicks under her and settled down to brood, calling as she had done earlier, but with less urgency. She looked about her, turning her head this way and that, as if taking a keen interest in the passage of the occasional redshanks and peewits that were flying about the marsh. Then, after half an hour, she got up, walked a few paces from the nest, and flew, calling as she went. She began to hunt, and almost immediately chanced upon something that took her attention, for she suddenly turned upwards to arrest herself in flight and quickly corkscrewed down to the ground. She must have been unsuccessful, however, for she rose again at once and continued to hunt. On she went, to and fro across the marsh, until she was lost to view, but within ten minutes she came in sight again, working her way carefully along the edge of a dyke. Here we saw her dive suddenly to the ground, and, after a brief disappearance, rise, carrying a small rodent in her talons. She carried it to one of her favourite perching posts, passing it up to her bill just as she was about to alight; and then, without ceremony, swallowed it whole.

The sun was now sinking towards the blue-grey mists that shrouded the distant horizon and the air was rapidly taking on that chilling touch that comes with the passing of an early-summer day. The young short-eared owls were calling vigorously with a wheezy, hunger note, and the smallest was trying to crawl under its larger brothers for warmth. We saw the cock bring a vole to the perch some little distance off, and alight with it still in his talons. The hen flew towards him, but he slipped away and she gave chase. This action appears to have been in the nature of play for soon both birds alighted together in the thick grass out of our sight. The cock left after a few seconds, but the hen remained down for about two minutes and must have swallowed the vole during that time, for neither bird carried anything away with it. The hen returned direct to the nest.

Plate 58.—Short-eared owl—aggressive attitude (*daylight*).

She resumed brooding for a short time, but, at about 9.40 she got up deliberately and left quickly. We had not heard the cock call to her, but she must have heard him, for, within two minutes she was back at the nest with a young decapitated vole in her bill. She dropped the vole in the nest, stood over the young and began feeding them. The eldest chick was still sleepy from the effects of the previous meal, and this time the smaller chicks received the major share of the food. The meal lasted about three minutes and concluded with the hen swallowing any scraps that remained. The nest tidied to her satisfaction, she crouched over the chicks and began to brood them, and she was still in this posture when the light having faded from the sky, we left the hide and made our way homeward.

85

The following day we spent the morning and the evening watching the short-eared owls and noticed that the chicks were being brooded less than on the previous occasions. In the evening, the hen was off the nest when we arrived about seven o'clock, and, judging by the dirty condition of the nest, we were of the opinion that she must have been away a considerable time. She returned at 7.40 p.m. and had some difficulty in persuading the chicks to settle. They seemed already to be asserting some independence, but she eventually raked them into position with her bill and tucked them under her.

It is remarkable how regular the short-eared owls are in this first visit to the nest with food. Over and over again during several breeding seasons in Norfolk, we have noted the cock as arriving at the nest within a few minutes of eight o'clock, and, in fact, Jim Vincent found the nest by deliberately choosing this time of day to watch the owls, and he often commented on this peculiarity. Precisely at eight o'clock on this evening, the cock arrived at the nest just as he had done the previous day. He brought a meadow-pipit as an offering to the hen and

Plate 59.—Portrait of a short-eared owl (*daylight*).

there was the same frantic excitement and quivering as we had seen before, but the visit was perhaps even more brief—we timed it as 3 seconds. The hen took the meadow-pipit in her right foot and rested on the tarsus so that the foot was free to manipulate the food. She pulled pieces from the pipit while the young called excitedly. They all had some meat in due course, though once again the largest chick had an undue share. Often as we had seen it before, we were still amazed at the large quantity of feathers and bone swallowed with the meat, this being taken to assist digestion, but subsequently ejected from the mouth in the form of a pellet. At the end of the meal the hen swallowed what remained of the pipit, including the legs, and then, as usual, she and the chicks indulged in a short siesta. This was broken after ten minutes by the largest chick, who wriggled out from under the hen and began to retch violently. He brought up a large, but loosely compacted, pellet consisting chiefly of feathers. The hen promptly picked this up and swallowed it herself and then went on to pick a number of droppings from the surrounding rush and to swallow them. The cock and hen continued to call to each other while she was brooding, but he had paid no further visits to the nest when we terminated our vigil at 10.30 p.m.

We resumed our observations on the morning of May 30th, by which time the fine, sunny weather of the previous few days had given way to cooler conditions with a fresh wind blowing from the north-east and with a threat of rain in the air. Due, no doubt, to this more chilly weather, the hen had resumed brooding the chicks, and she sat tight as we approached the hide until we were quite close to her. With her head turned towards us she watched our every movement, and we had an exceptional opportunity of seeing that fascinating face with its staring eyes and black, hooked bill.

As we turned to get into the hide, the hen short-eared owl flew off and we paused to inspect the nest and chicks, now ten, nine, and eight days old. We noticed that, as birds so often do when the chicks are approaching the stage of leaving the nest, the hen was becoming less particular about nest-sanitation, and several pieces of excrement were lying around the nest and attached to the rush. There was now an interesting difference between the chicks. The eldest appeared about twice as big as the youngest, and while the latter was still covered in white down so thin on his back that the skin shewed through with a pinkish tint, the eldest was well covered in greyish-fawn down and had a fair showing of feathers. His face had blackish-brown markings on either side of the bill and a well-defined dark ring giving the first indication of the outline of the facial disk. We noticed, too, that the eldest chick had now lost its egg-tooth. The retention of this to about the ninth day struck us as particularly interesting as most birds lose it during the first two or three days.

We looked out from the hide and saw the three chicks huddled together in the nest. From time to time they made a faint hissing noise but they shewed no inclination to any activity whatever. This rather surprised us in view of the state of their development, but, as we realised later, it was probably part of the instinctive urge of these birds to be quiescent in the morning. After about twenty minutes the hen flew over the nest, uttering a soft "cuff-cuff" as she went. She circled round and flew in again against the wind, her head hanging downward to watch the ground. She alighted just in front of the nest and as she stood there, looking first at the chicks and then at the hide, we noticed how the golden yellow iris is specially striking when the pupil is contracted in daylight. At night when the pupil is enlarged, there is very little of the golden iris to be seen. After standing for a moment, she turned to attend to the chicks. Stepping carefully over them, she stood shielding them while a reed-bunting, scolding with a sharp "tsic-tsic", flew just over the nest, and then she worked her way round the chicks and gradually settled over them. Soon she was dozing peacefully with her head turned over one shoulder and her eyes partially closed, and we noticed that, now that the chicks were getting larger, she gave them room by propping herself up on the "wrist" joints of her wings which had, in consequence, a drooped appearance.

The light gradually deteriorated and the threatened rain began to fall during this spell of watching, until, by the middle of the morning, it was pouring quite heavily. Large drops of water stood on the owl's back and kept running in trickles off her wing feathers, but she seemed quite unperturbed, and did not change her attitude at all. The eldest chick occasionally poked his head out from under the hen's breast feathers and appeared to be doing a little preening, and it seemed to be only ourselves that noticed the rain as it made an ominous patter on the roof of the hide.

The evening turned out fine and we resumed our watching at 6.55 p.m. when we observed that the second chick, now nine days old, had just discarded the egg-tooth. It is an indication of the "tameness" of these owls that the hen was back on the nest at 7.8 and settled immediately over the chicks. After a brief spell of desultory cleaning round the nest, she began preening herself, and, in so doing, she displayed the fine expanse of golden sandy wing and the individual beauty of her feathers as she spread them over her back. In the course of preening she stopped repeatedly to croak a soft "wherr-ack," lifting her head as she did so as if calling to her mate. Presently she left the nest, calling as she went, and she spent some time hunting across the marsh in the company of the cock.

The chicks were now getting quite active in her absence, pecking at each other's, as well as at their own, down. There was a good deal of shuffling about in the nest, the youngest chick, in particular, trying repeatedly to bury its head under the others. The adults could be heard calling from time to time as they beat about the marsh, but the youngsters appeared to take no notice of this. The eldest, especially, continued to preen himself vigorously, standing up at times

88

[*Continued on page* 90.

Plate 60.—Short-eared owl (*flashlight*).

Plate 61.—Short-eared owl with young (*daylight*).

and stretching his wings a little. We were surprised at their size. The wing span must already have been about twelve inches.

We have commented before on the effects of wet weather in limiting the food caught by those birds of prey that feed upon rodents, and this evening seemed to give further confirmation of our earlier observations. Although, as a rule, these birds had hunted without difficulty and had, with noticeable regularity, brought food to the nest about 8 o'clock, it was, on this occasion, 9.25 before anything was brought for the chicks. At 9.20 the hen got up from brooding, stepped forward off the nest and then flew, calling as she went. She must have been called off by the cock, for five minutes later she was back with a field-vole in her bill and began at once to feed this to the chicks. She stood astride them, as is the habit with the owls, and, tearing pieces of meat from the vole which she held under her left foot, she dangled the meat just in front of the chicks' mouths. This procedure is different from that of the diurnal birds of prey, which stand on the edge of the nest and face their chicks.

The meal was, unfortunately, interrupted by our relief who came to fetch us from the hide, but we were interested to see the hen's reactions to his approach. She stopped feeding and stood over the chicks, and then settled down on to them, all the time keeping her head facing in his direction. As he got nearer, her ear-tufts, which up to then had not been visible, were slowly erected, and were fully up when he came in her view. She stayed on the nest until he was quite close, and then, with a powerful spring, she leapt up and flew away.

The young owls were developing rapidly now, and each day we could notice the change in their appearance. By June 2nd, when they were thirteen, twelve, and eleven days old, they were all well covered in long down. It was buff, mottled with blackish-brown on their backs, and brownish-white, with a slight dark mottling, on the undersides. The faces, especially that of the eldest chick, were now more strikingly marked, a black patch extending each side of the black beak, and including both eyes. Between the eyes and above the bill, the down on the forehead was deep buff colour. This extended outwards to the edge of the facial disk, interrupted only by a thin curved black "eyebrow" rather to the side of each eye. The eyes, themselves, appeared royal blue at this stage, but already shewed the bright orange iris as in the adult.

It was evening when we were watching these chicks and they were somewhat restive as if anxious for a meal. The eldest was sitting up and swaying his head from side to side, and looking upwards with an expectant gaze. He opened his beak wide and revealed the delicate pink colour of the mouth lining. Every now and again the mouth quivered as if in immediate anticipation of food, but this was not yet forthcoming as both adults were away in the distance, hunting at the time. In accord with the habit to which we have already referred, the hen came flying across the marsh at about 8.20 p.m. and, swinging round the hide, alighted in front of the nest. She brought with her a short-tailed field-vole, which was given whole (complete with head) to the middle-sized chick, who swallowed it head-first. Strangely enough, there was no very great excitement on the part of the chicks as the hen approached. They turned to look up at her as she passed over, and greeted her with open mouths as she arrived at the nest, but there was none of the frantic struggling and clamouring that is so often seen when food is brought to young passerine chicks.

The hen stayed only a short time at the nest and then went off to resume her hunting; and the chicks resigned themselves to further waiting and passed some of the time in preening themselves. They continually inter-

91   [Continued on page 94.

Plate 62.—Hen short-eared owl swallowing a meadow-pipit the cock has just given her (*daylight*).

Plate 63.—Short-eared owl holding a field-vole in her bill. The young can be seen under her (*flashlight*).

Plate 64.—Short-eared owl "winking" (*daylight*).

Plate 65.—The aggressive attitude of a hen short-eared owl as she watches a cock Montagu's harrier fly overhead (*daylight*).

rupted this, however, to gaze around as if expecting another visit from the hen.

It was a still, quiet evening now, especially remarkable after the strong winds that had prevailed during the day, and, as we waited and watched, the sound of the marsh came pleasantly across the rushes. The skylarks were singing continuously, and the monotonous, plaintive note of the cuckoo was repeated with hardly a pause. A cow mooed at the distant farm and the jarring squawk of a cock pheasant broke into the background of bird song. At 8.55 we saw the cock Montagu's harrier again as he came beating low across the rushes. He has a majestic flight with his great wing span terminating in the well-marked wing-tip feathers which separate like the fingers of a hand as he glides after each few powerful strokes. The lovely grey of his graceful wings and long tail caught the light of the evening sun as he swerved close by us, but he was soon gone from our limited field of view.

As we turned our attention back to the nest in front of us, we saw that the young owls were nestling peacefully, but even when apparently resting they took a keen interest in what went on around them. They had become quite sensitive to any unusual noises, and followed intently the flight of any passing bird, even the abundant and harmless little meadow-pipit. This was a marked development of their interest in the outside world, and it heralded their departure from the nest. Two days later the two eldest chicks were out among the rush near the nest and only the youngest had not yet ventured forth; and they had all departed when we visited the nest on June 6th. On that occasion we could not find the young owls anywhere, though the parents were much in evidence. They had become markedly aggressive towards strangers at this time, and, though they made no attempt to mob us, they made several attacks on other people who visited the nest. Our friend, John Markham, for instance, was actually struck on the shoulder by one of the adults while he was looking at the nest; and the late Mr. H. F. Witherby was attacked on two occasions while examining the plumage coloration of the young.

Our last sight of these birds was on June 12th when the chicks were about three weeks old. We went across to dismantle the hide and saw the hen in the vicinity. She was looking very worn and bedraggled as a result of her family cares and she had lost several feathers from her wings. How very different from the sleek and beautiful bird she had been at the beginning of the season. We searched around and found one of the chicks resting under a thick tussock of rush sixty-four paces away fom the nest. It was almost fully feathered though a considerable amount of down was still attached, but it was not yet able to fly and was still dependent on its parents for food. The ability to fly must soon have developed, however, for shortly after this we could find no sign of the short-eared owl family on the marsh and we presumed they had begun the nomadic wanderings which are characteristic of the species for the greater part of their lives.

94

Plate 66.—Young short-eared owl stretching itself (*daylight*).

Plate 67.—Young short-eared owl at twenty-two days of age (*daylight*).

The Tawny Owl

THE TAWNY OWL, known also as the "brown owl" and "wood owl," is, to many people, familiar because of its hooting call. This is the only one of our owls with a true hoot, and it is, perhaps, best known on account of this; but, it should be noticed, the hoot is not the traditional "tu-whit, tu-whit, tu-whoo." The hoot of the tawny owl is a musical "hoo-hoo-hoo," followed, after a short interval, by a tremulous, and rather high-pitched, "oooooooo." It is most in evidence from January till the end of May, but it is often heard again in the autumn, at which season, the tawny owl, like many other birds, gives a performance only slightly inferior to that which resounds through the woods in spring. The hoot is, in effect, the song of the tawny owl, and has, to a large extent, the normal functions of bird song, being used to proclaim the ownership of territory, and also, as we shall presently describe, as an instrument of courtship.

Woodlands, wooded gardens, and other well-timbered places are the usual haunts of the tawny owl, and in such places the bird is to be found over most of Great Britain. It does not, however, seem to occur in the Orkneys, Shetlands or Outer Hebrides, and it is practically unknown in Ireland. This is rather remarkable, for, as we remarked in chapter 4, Ireland is a stronghold of the long-eared owl which has the same, almost exclusively nocturnal, habit as the tawny owl, and has a very similar diet. Villages and towns, as well as the more rural areas, give sanctuary to the tawny owl, and it is even to be found in the wooded suburbs of most of our large cities. We have, indeed, been told of tawny owls right in the heart of London, where, on moonlight nights, fireguards have seen them hunting the rats that prowled in the open across some of the bombed and devastated areas.

Where it nests, as it not infrequently does, in proximity to dwellings, the tawny owl sometimes causes quite a disturbance; breaking the sleep of nearby residents by a persistent emanation of hideous noises that, to the uninitiated, suggest the presence of something from another world. During the latter part of June and throughout July, some friends of ours in a London suburb were kept awake night after night by weird hissings and snoring noises that seemed to come out of the garden. They asked us to investigate, and though we guessed the cause of their trouble, we went to reassure them. It was a family of young tawny owls, not long out of the nest. They flew at dusk into one of the garden trees and there, hidden by foliage, they sat and called impatiently to their parents to hurry back with food; but food did not still those lusty youngsters for long, and the distracting chorus went on intermittently well into the small hours of the morning.

The tawny owl is seldom seen about by day unless it is accidentally disturbed from its roosting perch. It spends the daylight hours in a hollow tree or, as we shew in plate 68, perched on a bough with its body pressed close up against the

Plate 68.—Tawny owl perched in a beech tree (*daylight*).

trunk, though the roost is generally rather more concealed in ivy or foliage than is the one in our picture. As we walk through a wood near a roosting owl it remains immobile except that its head turns to follow our movements, and it relies to a large extent on this immobility to escape notice. Many a person must unknowingly have passed close by such a tawny owl as we depict and yet have been unaware of its presence.

Like certain other birds, the tawny owl varies considerably in plumage. There are two quite distinct types; one predominantly rufous, and the other greyish-brown, and there are variations between these two extremes. The rufous bird is by far the most common in this country though the grey variety is more usual on the Continent. When seen perched in a good light, a typical rufous tawny owl is an attractive-looking bird. The brown facial disk, with its very dark eyes, is well defined by a narrow rim of light feathers and is relieved by small light-coloured "eye-brows" set on either side of a narrow wedge of dark brown which extends downwards from the forehead to the base of the horn-coloured bill. The breast is a deep buff colour, shading to a paler hue towards the tail and is boldly marked with irregular longitudinal streaks of dark brown. Though the bird sits in a very upright posture, the back is less easily seen from below. It is a deep chestnut colour with dark markings on many of the individual feathers,

Plate 69.—Tawny owl giving chick a field-vole. The nest was in a rabbit hole (*flashlight*).

and with light flecks on some of the secondaries, giving noticeable light bars across the wings.

It is at dusk that we most often see the tawny owl in flight. He then appears as a large dark bird with a disproportionately large head and with broad, well-rounded wings. Like the other owls, he flies with a silent, buoyant flight with a noticeable undulating tendency, but unlike them, he shews a distinct tendency to keep within easy reach of the shelter of trees.

Trees, in fact, seem almost indispensable to the tawny owl, and though an occasional bird will nest in old masonry, the vast majority of them use hollow trees for nesting. They seem to like fairly large holes with easy access, especially holes that go down a little way below the entrance. Where such holes are not available, the tawny owl will use the old nests of such birds as carrion crow, magpie, and jay, and we have known it to resort to the use of a large rabbit hole. This was in Inverness-shire in 1940, when, towards the end of May, we found the nest with three well-grown chicks. The site was a small wood of mixed growth which did not provide any of the more favoured nesting places, and, because of that, we believe the rabbit hole was a regular haunt of these owls. At the time we saw them, the young were sufficiently advanced to be running out of the hole to meet the parents when they returned with food. In fact, they ran considerable distances from the mouth of the hole although they were still only in down at the time. They were being fed on rats, field-voles, and long-tailed field-mice, which, except for the larger rats, were being swallowed whole. We were interested to notice that, as we shew in a photograph taken near the entrance to the nesting hole, the parents closed their eyes while passing the prey to the chicks. Was this, we wondered, to prevent the chicks, in their eagerness, from damaging the parents' eyes.

Plate 70.—Tawny owl's nest and eggs on ground.

Interesting as this nest in the rabbit hole proved to be, we were unable to see as much as we should have liked because of the advanced age of the chicks. We were much more fortunate, however, in 1943, when Mrs. I. M. Thomson, in company with Jim Vincent, found, in Norfolk, a nest with four eggs in what we believe to be a unique position. It was on the ground, among the dead bracken in a small clearing in a wood. The bird had made a crude attempt at nest building, using dry oak leaves to form a shallow saucer, and in this she had laid her four white eggs. They looked absurdly conspicuous lying there open to the sky, for at this time of year (the nest was found on April 27th) the trees were not yet in leaf and the new bracken had not yet uncurled its fronds.

It was 11th May before we saw any sign of hatching. On this occasion the hen was sitting unusually tight, and when she left we found that the first egg was chipping. Two decapitated young rats were on the nest—the first we had seen there, and another instance of the first food coinciding with the imminence of hatching of the young. The chick was out of its shell, but was still damp, when we saw it the following day, so it is fairly certain that the first hatching occurred on May 12th. There was, on this occasion, a good deal more food around the nest, and we counted three adult water-voles, one long-tailed field-mouse, one young rat, and one adult water-shrew.

We began detailed observation at this nest on the evening of May 14th, when there were two chicks, two days and one day old, and still two eggs not yet hatched. There was a freshly killed and decapitated three-quarter-grown rat by the nest when we arrived shortly before dusk, and it seemed that the owls must have begun hunting early that evening. Conditions were certainly right for hunting, for it was cool, but beautifully still, after a very hot day, and it was likely that the rodents were out early. The two young owls were squealing almost continuously as we entered the hide, but the hen came back very shortly after our arrival and went straight on to the nest to brood the chicks, who immediately became quiet. The hen, herself, closed her eyes and appeared to go to sleep. A few birds could be heard in the distance, piping their last songs before the close of the day, but in the wood itself there was an utter silence, save only for an occasional rustle in the dry undergrowth as some little nocturnal creature went about his business.

The daylight faded, and the sky deepened to a rich, inky blue against which the stars stood out in twinkling brilliance. The moon was mounting higher in the sky, and piercing the black and tangled canopy of boughs and branches, to flood the wood with a weak and ghostly light, patterned with dark and twisted shadows of fantastic shape. The tawny owl sat there, quiet and motionless, on her nest amid the bracken, and we, the unseen watchers of this eerie scene, kept silence with the wood. An hour and a half passed slowly by, when suddenly the quiet was shattered by a sharp "ke-wick," which jerked us to a high pitch of

 [Continued on page 102.

Plate 71.

Plate 72.

Plate 73.

Plate 71.—Tawny owl—expression by night.
Plate 72.—Expression by day.
Plate 73.—Calling to its mate (*flashlight*).

101

expectancy. It was the cock tawny owl, who, approaching unseen and unheard, had called from a tree a little to our left. The hen woke instantly, and, turning her head, replied to him with a soft mewing note.

For the next few minutes the two birds kept up a duet, the hen using her soft, cat-like mewing, and the cock his sharper and louder "ke-wick," until presently he flew to a tree just behind the nest. We could see him clearly in the light of the moon, and we could observe how the hen became very excited, shivered her wings a little, and called more loudly and more rapidly. This behaviour lasted for four minutes, at the end of which the hen flew from the nest and alighted by the cock, who passed her the food he was carrying. As soon as the cock bird had thus disposed of the prey, he left the perch and for a short time flew in small circles round his mate, calling excitedly to her as she sat there. Finally he flew to a tree just behind the hide, but out of our sight, and gradually lapsed into silence. The hen continued to call for a few minutes and then planed down to the nest, carrying the food (a field-vole) in her bill. She settled over the young and was still brooding them when, an hour later, we left the hide.

It was then close on midnight, but such a perfect night for observation that we greatly regretted we had not come prepared to stay out till daybreak. As we made our way homeward, we remarked again on the silence in the wood and contrasted it with the comparatively noisy bustle of such a night in the open. Out across the marsh the redshanks were calling continuously, and the sedge-warblers were chattering and scolding almost as if it were day. A sandpiper was heard, and a water-rail squealed and groaned in the thick sedge; while in the distance, bitterns were booming out their melancholy notes. But owls were our quest, and, as if to remind us of this, a barn-owl flew just in front of us across our path and seemed to challenge us with its eerie, ghost-like shriek.

The following evening we came to the hide prepared to stay the whole night, for it promised to be fine again and the moon was now nearly full. There were still only two chicks, though the third egg was well chipped. For the first hour the hen brooded quietly with her back towards us, and in that position she was extraordinarily difficult to see, in spite of the bright moonlight, the mottling on her back matching the dappled surroundings under the conditions of almost monochromatic vision that exist when the human eye is dark-adapted.

The first activity occurred at 10.15 p.m., B.D.S.T., when the hen, after calling softly for a few minutes, flew from the nest to a nearby tree. She began to call loudly now, and repeatedly, using her familiar "ke-wick, ke-wick"; and we thought she must be calling to the cock, though we were puzzled that she should call for food, as there was a half-grown decapitated rat by the nest when we arrived. The cock did not answer her, and after a few flights from tree to tree she went farther afield in the direction of some rough ground overgrown with brambles and hawthorns. We knew this place to be the haunt of numerous small birds; and the existence there of countless rabbit holes, and rat and vole runs, made it appear a promising hunting ground. There is little doubt that the hen hunted there, for in twelve minutes, that is, at 10.27, she was back at the nest with a young fledged blackbird in her bill. This food was given to the young, the hen standing over them and feeding them in exactly the same manner as we described in the case of the long-eared owl on page 64. As she passed down each piece of food, the hen chuckled very softly to the chicks—so softly that it was just discernable in the hide and certainly could not have been heard more than a few yards away. The young kept up a constant whistling noise for the first part of the feed, which lasted for about twenty minutes.

With the conclusion of the meal, everything became quiet again in the wood and the next two hours passed by very slowly; but while our gaze was concentrated on the immobile form of the brooding tawny owl, our thoughts went out to the open spaces beyond the wood. There, as on the previous night, the wild life seemed very much awake in the bright moonlight, and there was hardly a moment

[*Continued on page* 105.

Plate 74.—The cock tawny owl brings a rat to the hen (*flashlight*).

Plate 75.—Tawny owl with remains of young rabbit (*flashlight*).

Plate 76.—The hen brings a water shrew to the nest—another water shrew and a water-vole may also be seen by the side of the young (*flashlight*).

that was not filled with sound. The residents were there, and the water-rails, especially, were even more noisy than before, but in addition we noticed many small parties of waders obviously still passing through the district to complete their northward migration.

At 12.50 a.m. the hen tawny owl must have seen or heard the cock approach, for she suddenly called. He answered at once, and the two birds kept up a conversational duet for about five minutes. Then the cock, with food dangling from his bill, dropped down by the side of the hen. Both birds appeared to be intensely excited. The cock slowly flapped his wings up and down and the hen puffed out her feathers and quivered them rapidly; and all the time the two birds kept up a soft but rapid calling. In the midst of this display, E. J. H. fired a flash-bulb and obtained the record shewn in plate 74, but the birds took not the slightest notice. The cock approached the hen, leaned forward and passed her the food, which we were able to identify as a decapitated half-grown rat, and then flew off, calling "ke-wick" sharply and loudly as he went.

There was little other activity at the tawny owls' nest that night. A dark shadow, cast by a tree, crept across the sitting hen and for a time we were unable to see much detail of what occurred, but we believe she swallowed the rat that the cock had brought to her. At 1.30 a.m. a rustling took our attention and we made out a rat prowling about not far from the nest. The hen tawny owl became extremely interested and sat bolt upright, and we wondered what action she would take; but the rat moved away and the incident passed off without further excitement. The hen continued brooding throughout the rest of the night, and on three more occasions called to the cock, but he had not been back again to the nest when we left at 5.15 a.m. and the chicks had, it seemed, had only one feed in the course of the night.

Two days later we spent another complete night with these owls and noticed much the same general procedure. There was an initial period of brooding, but this time the cock must have come back to a tree near the nest a little before 11.20 p.m. for at that time the hen called and he immediately answered. The two birds continued to call to each other in a rising frenzy till the wood resounded to their cries, and then the hen flew from the nest to where the cock was perched. At this the calls reached a climax of intensity and excitement. The hen took the food from her mate and flew with it to an adjacent tree. As before, the cock flew away directly he had given up the food, and the hen, after a few moments, returned to the nest, where the young were now "chittering" as if hungry.

The hen fed the young on pieces torn from the prey she had just brought in. All three chicks had a share, for the food was more than enough for them all at this age; and although the eldest had the lion's share at first, he soon became gorged and sank down into the nest, giving his weaker brethren an opportunity to receive their fill. The meal was a leisurely affair, with several brief intervals,

105

[*Continued on page* 107.

Plate 77.—A tawny owl with food at nesting hole (*flashlight*).

and lasted in all about twenty-five minutes, terminating just before midnight.

During this vigil, which lasted till 5 a.m. we saw a further meal given to the young. This began at 2.37 a.m. when the hen, after an absence of twenty-two minutes, brought in a newly-fledged blackbird which, presumably, she had caught herself. We noticed that, although the chicks were only five, four, and two days old, they were being given feathers with the meat. This "roughage" seems to be an essential item in the owls' diet, and we were reminded of a young tawny owl which, after meeting with an accident, was cared for by a school. The scholars, unwittingly, fed the bird on liver and raw meat, and yet it died; whereas another which, at a later date, was brought up on a diet which included mice, grew satisfactorily and eventually was liberated to the wild.

Again we had a night off from owl watching, and next visited the nest on May 19th when the young were seven and six days old. The youngest chick and the egg were missing and we wondered what had become of them. When we arrived at 10 p.m., we found three water-shrews by the nest, all of them rear halves only;

[*Continued on page* 110.

Plate 78.—Tawny owl breeding site, showing nesting tree and observer's hide.

Plate 79.—Tawny owl brings a water-vole to the nest (*flashlight*).

Plate 80.—Young tawny owls (*flashlight*).

and we noticed that the elder chick now had his eyes open and had discarded the egg-tooth. The younger had his eyes closed and still retained the egg-tooth.

We saw two feeds that night, but the most interesting features during our watch were certainly the courtship displays that took place on two occasions. The first was at 12.55 a.m. when the cock, from somewhere near the nest, called to the hen, who was brooding at the time. She answered with a short note—"twit," it might be written—and then followed a duet, each replying to the other's call. Faster and faster, louder and louder, became the performance, until the whole wood seemed to ring from end to end. Suddenly it would stop. Quiet would reign for a few seconds, only to be broken by a renewal of this frantic calling. The duet lasted, more or less continuously, for ten minutes, and we had the impression that the hen was trying to call the cock down to the nest, while he was equally trying to persuade her up to him on his perch. If this was so, the lady had her way, for suddenly, albeit silently, the cock alighted at the nest, dropped some food in front of her, and was gone again in a flash. The hen continued to call after him for some minutes, but without effect, till presently the wood returned to quiet again.

It was at 2.3 a.m. that the cock began to call again from just above the nest. A duet, like that described above, took place and lasted for eight minutes, but this time the hen flew up to where the cock was perched. As she alighted by his side, so he flew, and she quickly took off again in pursuit. We could hear the chase continuing through the wood. Round and round the birds flew, rising and dipping, and calling all the time with a variety of notes that must be heard to be believed. All the calls of the tawny owl seemed to be included in this medley of noise—hoots and mewings, gurglings, and sharp, piercing cries. It was a vocal display such as we have never heard the like. Whether the birds were chasing each other, or whether the cock was always the pursued, we could not determine by the light of the moon, but we can be sure that the hen did at least catch up with the cock at some time as, directly after the display, she came back to the nest with a small rodent which she fed to the chicks.

On the afternoon of May 21st, we visited the tawny owls' nest, and, as we approached, we saw the hen fly up. On reaching the nest, however, we were astonished to find both owlets missing. There was nothing but the remains of a young rabbit. This puzzled us, and we wondered whether the rat we had seen prowling near the nest was anything to do with the disappearance; but if so, why was the hen tawny owl still sitting? She had certainly flown up a few minutes earlier. We came away dejected, and happening to encounter Jim Vincent that evening, mentioned the matter to him. His curiosity was roused and off we all set for another inspection of the nest. Again we saw the hen fly up, but still there was no sign of any chick; neither was there even the remains of the rabbit now. That, too, was missing.

110   [Continued on page 112.

Plate 81.—Cock tawny owl holding a field-vole in his bill (*flashlight*).

Jim Vincent, prompted by his long experience in field craft, began to clear the bracken from around the nest and presently found the largest owlet still alive and apparently unharmed. Further search revealed no trace of the other chicks or of the missing egg, but, turning our attention back to the nest itself, we discovered a hole that came up right into the bottom of the nest. It appeared to be the work of either a rat or a stoat so we began opening it up and tried to follow its course. It went deeper and turned, however, and, having no spade available, we had to abandon the task. We felt sure, now, that we had found the solution to the mystery, but even this posed further problems. Why had the adult tawny owl not been able to prevent this from happening when, in the ordinary way, she was more than a match for these rodents? Would she have been unable to attack the rat because of the position of the young owls, or did the unusual circumstances frighten her and upset her reactions?

We made several more visits to the vicinity to observe the progress of the tawny owls, and a week later, when the chick was sixteen days old, we found it several feet away from where the nest had been. It was then shewing feathers over most of its body. It was an aggressive little creature and snapped at a finger held out to it. Then, when we went to pick it up, it clicked its bill; at which signal, the hen, who had been watching us from a tree a little way off, dived down at great speed and flew straight at us. We had had, as we shall presently relate, some experiences of the attack of a tawny owl, and this one, we thought, looked distinctly dangerous. We waved our arms, but she did not deviate from her course, until, when almost within our reach, she swerved upwards and flew into another tree. She snapped her bill angrily and called, and began working her feet on the perch as if she were contemplating another attack, so, thinking discretion the better part of valour, we beat a hasty retreat.

This nest in the open was, as we have said, extremely unusual for the tawny owl, but we have described it in some detail because of the exceptional opportunity it gave us of seeing what took place. A more typical nesting site is shewn in plate 78. This nest was in a hollow tree in a coppice of mixed growth, and the general behaviour of the birds was, in most respects, very similar to that which we have already described. Feeding habits were essentially the same, though, because we were able to watch the young throughout the whole of their fledging period, we sometimes saw as many as six and seven feeds in the course of a night when the young were nearly ready to fly. For instance, one night when the chicks were nearly four weeks old, we found three fresh half-grown rats on the nest when we arrived at 9.30 p.m. The hen brought in the rear half of another young rat at 10.25 p.m. and gave this to one of the chicks who quickly swallowed it; and at 10.57 p.m. she returned again with a field-vole, which was swallowed by another of the chicks. No further visits were paid to the nest till 1.57 a.m. when the hen arrived with a half-grown rat. This was given to the smallest chick,

 [Continued on page 114.

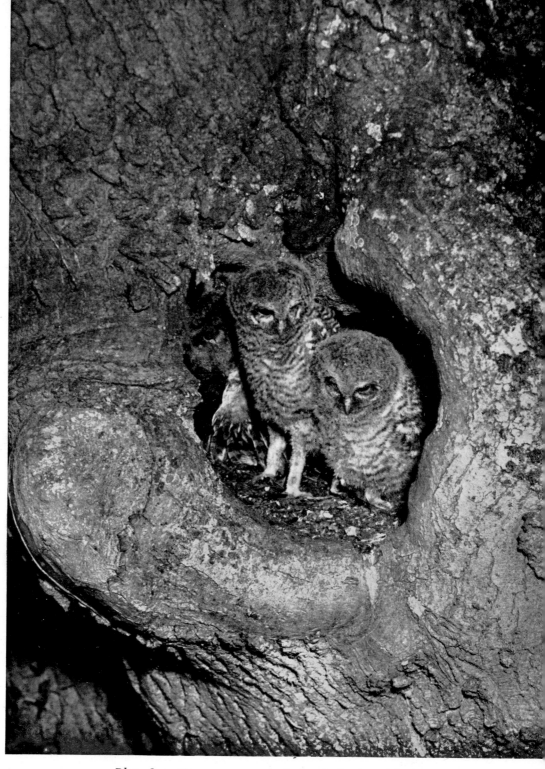

Plate 82.—Young tawny owls in their nest (*flashlight*).

who, to our surprise, swallowed it. If the chicks were able to tackle food of this size, why, we wondered, had they not touched the three rats that were on the nest when we arrived. The chicks were quite active at this time and were able to climb about the tree, so there is no doubt that they could get at the rats if they wanted to.

Events were to arouse our curiosity still further, but not to satisfy it, for, at 2.9 a.m. the hen flew down to the hole and removed one of those rats. Why did she do this? It was a fine night for hunting and she could easily have caught all the food she needed without drawing on what appeared to be reserves.

Both cock and hen were flying and calling in the vicinity of the nest just after 3 o'clock, and as the hen approached, the chicks called excitedly in chorus to her. She brought a mouse and gave it to one of them. Hunting must certainly have been easy, for at 3.28 a.m. she was back yet again; this time with a young rat which was taken by one of the chicks that was waiting right on the outside of the hole. We noted that the hen went into the hole and took away another of the original three rats.

A further visit was at 4.35 a.m. when it was beginning to get light. Both adults had still been very active about the wood and were calling frequently when suddenly the hen came down and perched on a post of the hide. The three young all became very excited, and, when the hen flew down to them a moment later, there was a scuffle to get the prey—another young rat. The last visit of the night was at 5.15 a.m. when the hen brought another rat and gave it to the middle-sized chick.

Summarizing the night's observations, we see that food was brought to the nest on seven occasions in addition to the visits necessary to bring in the three rats that were there when we arrived. This increased activity still only provided about two meals for each chick, for, as we have recorded, the prey was now swallowed whole, and only one chick could be fed at each visit. It will have been noticed that, during this period of observation, all the food was brought in by the hen, but this was not always the case. On several other occasions the cock himself delivered the prey to the nest, but his visits were comparatively infrequent and were always brief.

It is not possible to give a complete list of food consumed by a family of tawny owls in the wild state, for much of it is caught and eaten at once and cannot be seen except on really bright moonlight nights. It may, however, be interesting to tabulate what we have actually seen as this will probably indicate the relative proportions of the various items in the diet of the young tawny owls.

Rat	17
Short-tailed field-vole	5
Water-vole	5
Water-shrew	5
Rabbit	5

Long-tailed field-mouse	3
Young blackbird	2
Young pheasant	1
Young red-legged partridge	1

Before leaving the tawny owl, we should perhaps utter a word of caution about the aggressive habits of this bird during the breeding season. We have no wish to cause general alarm, for, in the normal way the tawny owl keeps well to herself and avoids human beings; but lest our accounts of watching the owls should stimulate others to do likewise, we should make it clear that many tawny owls will not tolerate undue interference with their young, and will attack even human beings who molest them.

There are numerous cases on record of people who have been attacked and sometimes injured, and we ourselves had a nasty experience in 1937 in the course of photographing a pair of these birds. We had been working from a tall hide and were climbing up the scaffolding framework to dismantle the photographic apparatus, when suddenly, out of the pitch darkness and before we were even aware of her presence, the owl struck. She must have dived silently beneath the hide platform and between the poles to deliver her attack, and as she sailed close by E. J. H., she extended a talon and penetrated his left eye. There was nothing for it but to get him as quickly as possible to a doctor and from there to hospital, but not even the wonders of modern ophthalmic surgery could repair the damage wrought by the owl, and he had to lose an eye.

So it is that now we always wear some form of head protection when working on tawny owls in the dark, and we advise anybody else to do the same. An old fencing mask looks clumsy, but gives excellent protection, or a suitable shield can be improvised from wire netting or from a sheet of one of the transparent plastics. Many people will go through their bird-watching days without being attacked, but the risk is there, and if our word of advice can prevent the repetition of our own misfortune, it will not have been written in vain.

Here we must leave our study of the owls in their native haunts, where for these several years we have watched them by day and night in our efforts to obtain pictures and facts of their fascinating lives. We pass finally to a consideration of the structural peculiarities of their eyes and ears which enable them to be true "birds of the night."

The Eyes and Ears of Owls

by STUART SMITH

OWLS are the most nocturnal of all birds and since, taken generally, birds are lovers of the light, it is only in exceptional cases that certain types have adapted themselves to nocturnal requirements, and made the night their day. The owls have passed from diurnal to nocturnal habits by evolution through crepuscular birds like the goatsuckers and American frog-mouths, and in these latter types we can trace the same soft plumage and large eyes which also characterize the owls. Since they live by catching animal prey in conditions of extremely low light-intensity, owls may be expected to have developed very definite modifications of eye and ear to adapt them to the strange conditions of " seeing in the dark" and of hearing the most minute of sounds.

Let us consider first how such evolutionary adaption has modified the eyes of owls. Even on the darkest nights, which appear to the human eye as absolutely

SWAN   TAWNY OWL   ADULT MAN

Fig. 1.—Cross section of eyes of swan, tawny owl and man—life size.

black, there are present very small amounts of light, and it is obviously essential for the owl to make the most of every scrap of available illumination. The dimmest light must be trapped to the maximum possible extent, and having been trapped, must be utilised by the recording mechanism of the owl's eye to the greatest possible degree. If we now come to compare the eye of an owl with that of a diurnal bird, we find that nature has so adapted the owl's eye that it brilliantly fulfills the required conditions. In Fig. 1 are shown in cross-section, for comparison at life-size, the eyes of a swan, tawny owl and a man. The relatively enormous size of the owl's eye compared with the swan's and the human eye, should be noted. That the eye of this owl is actually larger than the human eye is all the more striking when the relative sizes of the two heads are considered. This is well brought out by the photographs which show, in proportion, the eyes and heads of swan, tawny owl, and adult man. The small eye of the swan appears lost in its head, when compared with the eye of the owl. Notice also that the visible part of the owl's eye is almost entirely taken up by the iris in contradistinction to the human eye in which a considerable part of the front of the eye-ball is visible. We see therefore only a small portion of the eye of the owl, most of which is hidden within the structure of the skull. A large proportion of the owl's skull is thus occupied by the eyes, and these are so tightly jammed into the sockets that they cannot be moved, even by the application of considerable force. This lack of optical mobility might obviously be a serious drawback in a hunting bird, but it is beautifully compensated by the extraordinary ability of the owl to rotate its head. This rotability is of the order of three-quarters of a circle, as anyone knows who has walked round a tree containing a roosting owl in day-time! The bird's head follows you round until it is almost looking backwards.

One of the most striking characteristics of the eyes of owls is the way they face forward; they are, in fact, the most frontally facing eyes in the avian world. This is no mere chance, since frontal eyes give the binocular, and probably also stereoscopic, vision so essential for the accurate judging of distances. Thus owls have an angular field of binocular vision as high as 70 degrees, compared with only 24 degrees for the homing pigeon, whose eyes are set in the side of its head. The owl, swooping in the dark to take a rat or vole from the ground, must be able to judge distances to the finest degree; the pigeon, picking up grain and seeds in daylight, requires merely as wide a field of vision as possible. It is of interest to note here that whilst owls, most frontally seeing of all birds, are quite unable to move their eyes in the sockets, man, most frontal of all mammals, has the greatest eye movement.

An essential feature of the eye of any predatory bird is that it should be able to keep a sharply focused image of its prey continuously on the retina of the eye. In this respect, the owl's eye again shows beautiful adaptation, as do also the eyes of hawks, falcons, and other predatory birds, enabling them to follow the rapid twists and turns of their quarry. The ability of the eye to change its focus, and so keep a sharp image continuously on the retina in spite of changes in distance, is known as "accommodation." Great rapidity in accommodation is ensured in owls (and in hawks) by a particularly strong muscle known as "Crampton's muscle." This muscle can rapidly depress both the lens of the eye and the outer surface or "cornea," giving fine focusing almost instantaneously. But the employment of so strong and rapid a squeezing action within the eye sets up high intra-occular pressures, and, in order that these may not get out-of-hand and damage the soft eye-tissues, the corneal surface is surrounded by a ring of bony plates, known as the "scleral ossicles" which help the eye to deform without injury.

Another specially developed feature of the owl's eye is the *nictitating membrane*,

117   [*Continued on page* 120.

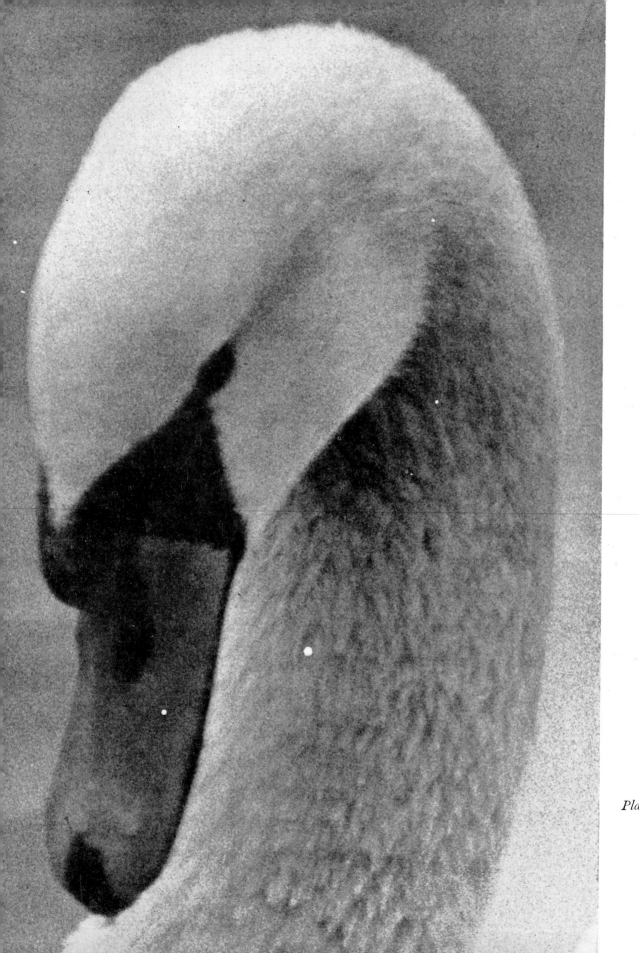

Plate 83.

Plate 84.

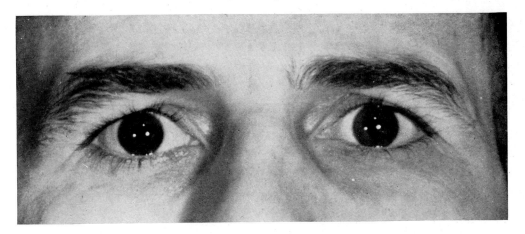

Plate 85.
Plate 83.—Head of mute swan—life size.
Plate 84.—Head of tawny owl—life size.
Plate 85.—Eyes of adult man—life size.

or third eye-lid. This is present in all birds, and in a great many vertebrates as well, and it is interesting to note that it remains in an atrophied form in the human eye as the *plica semi-lunaris*, which can be easily seen in a mirror as a crescent-shaped piece of skin lying behind the small fleshy "button" at the junction of the two eye-lids on the nasal side. The nictitans consists of a skin-like membrane (cloudy and opaque in owls but very transparent in all other birds except the dipper), with a lining of tiny pimple-like cells, and it is drawn across the eyeball from the nasal side to the other. Its function is to keep the surface of the eyeball polished and free from dirt and dust, whilst a marginal pleat on the outer surface of the membrane cleans the *under* surface of the eye-lids. The *nictitating membrane* in operation is shown in the photograph of a short-eared owl feeding young. The membrane is halfway across the eye, and will pass right across to the other corner and back again.

Since the owl's eye is relatively so large, and fits so snugly in its socket, the usual muscular system found in other birds for operating the *nictitating membrane* cannot find room within the owl's skull. Consequently the membrane in this bird is operated by a special tendon whose path travels round the outer orbit of the eye in a distinct groove and has, in fact, an action similar to that of a pulley which draws the membrane across and over the surface of the eye-ball. The action is usually a fairly rapid one, though not so rapid as the "blink" of a normal eye-lid. To close its eyes, the owl employs the *upper* lid as do human beings, and in this it differs from all other birds, since they use the *lower* lid for this purpose. We see then that by evolutionary changes, the owl's eye has arrived at a structural form whereby its large size, with consequent large iris and lens, enables it to trap to the maximum extent the small amounts of light available under nocturnal conditions. It now remains to be shewn how further highly specialised features of the owl's eye utilise this low light-intensity once it has passed through the lens of the eye.

The function of the lens in any eye is the same as that of a camera lens, namely to project an image on to a sensitive recording screen. In the photographic process, this is normally a plate or film coated with a chemical which is sensitive to light; in the vertebrate eye we find, instead, a membrane known as the *retina* which carries a large number of tiny cells which are light-sensitive. In the diurnal animal, these cells are normally of two kinds, known from their shapes as "cones" and "rods." The cones are the cells whereby we distinguish colours but they are operative only at relatively high intensities of light. At very low intensities, only the rods are able to record. In addition, the rods contain a remarkable substance known as rhodopsin or "visual purple." This is extremely light-sensitive, and, while it is itself decomposed by the energy of the light it absorbs, it converts that energy into a tiny electric current which sends an impulse through the rods to the brain.

     [*Continued on page* 122.

Plate 86.—Short-eared owl feeding young. Note position of nictitating eyelid (*daylight*).

Turning now to the owl's eye, we find developed within it a specific retinal structure which enables it to utilise to the full the smallest degree of illumination Thus we find that the owl's retina is one composed almost entirely of rods, with very few cones present. Moreover, these rods are extremely slender, compared with those of the human eye, so that a great many can be packed into a small area—there are as many as 56,000 per square millimeter in the retina of the tawny owl. Each of these rods carries the light-sensitive "visual purple" and, obviously the greater the number present over a given area, the greater the impulse sent to the brain by a given amount of light. But this is not all. The fibre cells which carry the impulse from the rods to the brain tend to run together and coalesce as they pass backwards from the retina, and hence we get the phenomenon of "summation" whereby many of the rods combine to send a highly amplified impulse to the brain for a comparatively small amount of light energy.

The retina of the owl's eye, which has a very high rod density and a high degree of "summation," is thus able to make the most of the extremely low illumination which obtains under nocturnal conditions. This ultra-high sensitivity to light in the eyes of owls is well demonstrated in the photographs which show the head and eyes of the long-eared owl photographed during the daytime and also by flashlight at night. It will be noticed that, under daylight conditions the pupils shrink to a small size; the owl's retina is too sensitive to cope with such a high intensity of light, and so the pupil is contracted to a small diameter to cut down the light entering the eye. But in the dark, the pupils expand to occupy practically the whole of the iris, giving that tremendous light-gathering power to which reference has already been made.

The study of the owl's retina leads us to ask whether these birds see colours as we do. The fact that this retina is composed almost entirely of slender rods, with few or no cones, points to the probability that owls cannot distinguish colours, since colours are detected by the cones. For these birds, the world should be one composed of various shades of grey, of differing brightness. Scientists experimenting with owls to test their colour-reactions, have substantially confirmed this view, the response of owls to light of differing wave-lengths fitting in with a cone-free and therefore colour-blind retina. Owls cannot distinguish blue from red, although they see blue as a brighter shade of grey than red of equivalent brightness, and this agrees again with a retina of high rod-density, since the visual purple within the rods does not absorb red.

In the eyes of all animals, there is normally a portion of the retina which is more sensitive than the rest. It is situated opposite the central part of the lens and is called the *area centralis* or more commonly, the *fovea*. In the majority of birds, the eyes are set more or less in the side of the head, and the pigeon, for example, uses its eyes in two ways. It can look straight out sideways with each eye, when they act independently and record two separate fields of view; or it can bring both eyes to bear together on an object in front of its head, when the two eyes combine to give a single binocular image. To meet these two possibilities, the retina of the diurnal bird is equipped with two *foveae* or sensitive spots, one for use with sideways vision, and the other for use with frontal vision. The owl, on the other hand, is limited to frontal vision only, since its eyes are facing forwards and cannot move in their sockets; and hence in the owl's retina we find only one *fovea*, the other being atrophied from lack of use.

The sight of all diurnal birds is extremely acute, and the whole mechanism is such that there is a tendency to over-work the retina which is required to distinguish, or "resolve," very minute objects. In order to aid the retina in its high metabolic demands, the eyes of birds are furnished with a bridge-like structure which projects from the base of the optic nerve into the interior of the eye. This structure, known as the *pecten*, is a mass of blood vessels, and it is believed that these act as a nutritive device to feed the retina and keep it "toned up." In owls, where the demands on the eye are much less stringent owing to the low light-intensities at which it normally operates, the *pecten* is of small size, and relatively undeveloped structurally, compared with the diurnal birds, and in this owls again show similarity to the nightjars and frogmouths.

In considering the means whereby owls can "see in the dark," there remains the possibility that something in the construction of the eyes of these birds might enable them to make use of "illumination" whose wave-lengths lie outside the scope of the human eye. Such "invisible light" we know exists, for it will affect a photographic plate, and is usually known as "ultra-violet" at the blue end of the spectrum, and "infra-red" at the red end. Even on the darkest night, infra-red radiation is present in measurable amounts due to terrestrial radiation. With this in mind, one scientist carried out some experiments with a tame tawny owl. This owl was kept in a dark room, and prey in the form of live mice were released, when the owl was shown to be able to catch the mice in conditions which looked quite dark to the human eye. It seemed that this might be due to the infra-red rays emitted from the body of the live mouse, due to its body-heat. If the mice were dead, the owl appeared unable to find them, as they were left untouched. Pieces of horseflesh placed before the owl in the dark room were not taken, but if they were placed near a source of infra-red rays, the owl immediately found and ate them. These results, at once startling and novel, have not, however, withstood the test of time. Further scientists have shown by use of a dissected owl's eye, that it is quite impossible for infra-red rays to reach the retina of the owl, since they are absorbed by the cornea and lens of the eye. In addition it has been demonstrated that the long-eared owl responds to the same wave-lengths of light, and in exactly the same way, as a human eye which has been "dark adapted," that is an eye which has become accustomed to the dark by being in it for some time. In other words, the rods which compose the owl's retina respond as do the human rods, but during day-time, the owl has no cones which it can bring into operation. Hence the evidence at present is that there is nothing in the owl's eye which would make it sensitive to infra-red radiation, and we can explain its splendid adaptation to nocturnal conditions in terms of an eye with a great light-gathering power and an ability to amplify that light to the maximum possible extent.

Turning now to the ears of owls, we again find considerable structural variation, not only compared with the ears of other birds, but also amongst the various species of the owl family. The reasons for the highly specialised and complex form of ear present in certain owls are by no means apparent, and although the structure of their ears has been well worked-out, we do not yet know what specific purposes are served by many of the queer and apparently anomalous features which have been evolved.

It is important to get clear in the first instance where the ears of owls are situated. They are *not* associated with the tufts of feathers which protrude from the forehead of certain species and which, for example, give the long- and short-eared owls their names, but are to be found at the side of the head rearward from the eyes. They are normally concealed by feathers which are often modified into stiff bristles. In comparison with the ears of most other birds, those of the owls, agree in one particular, in that they are large in proportion to the size of the bird, and this fact may be interpreted as an adaptation to enable the owl to detect the tiny sounds associated with the voices and movements of their prey. Beyond this broad and general fact, further attempts at interpreting the significance of the many structural peculiarities of ears of owls lead one into mere conjecture.

Starting with the most simple ears to be found in the owl family, we will consider the various species, in order of increasing complexity. Thus the snowy owl and the hawk-owl, both of which are largely diurnal in their habits have an external ear comparatively small and simple in form, though still large compared with truly diurnal birds. There are no very remarkable peculiarities, both ears being identical on either side of the head. The ears of the eagle-owl and those of the scops-owl are similar to the above, but have the openings conspicuously enlarged, though they still remain symmetrical on both sides of the head. Consideration of the ears of the barn-owl, however, leads us to the first major peculiarity for we find in this bird that the ears are covered by a large flap of skin, known as the "operculum," which is absent in the four species so far considered. This flap is very large in the barn-owl, and extends upwards and downwards to the extremities of the skull. It is much larger than would appear necessary, since the actual opening of the external ear is comparatively small, and its function remains obscure, although suggestions have been put forward that it can be raised to act as a kind of ear-trumpet, or to increase the resonance of sound. Increasing complexity occurs in the tawny owl, for here, not only are the ear openings (which

124 [*Continued on page* 126.

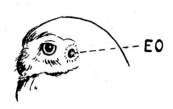

LITTLE OWL

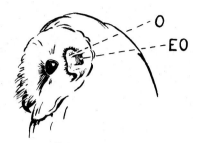

BARN OWL

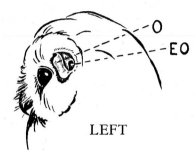

LEFT

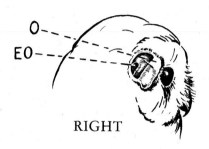

RIGHT

TAWNY OWL

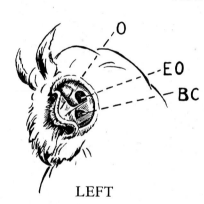

LEFT

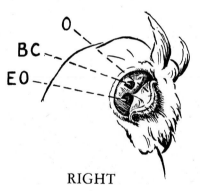

RIGHT

LONG EARED OWL

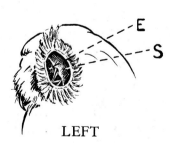

LEFT

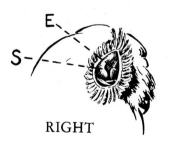

RIGHT

TENGMALM'S OWL

E O = EAR OPENING   B C = BLIND CAVITY
O = OPERCULUM   E = EYEBALL
                       S = SKULL

are very large in this bird) covered by an operculum or skin-flap, but the ears are not the same on the two sides of the head! The right ear is distinctly larger than, and of different shape from, the left, and this "asymmetry" as it is called, is by no means confined to this species. It is interesting to note that lizards also possess a skin-covering to the external ear, and in this similarity the owls have retained traces of their reptilian ancestry.

The ears of both the long- and short-eared owls have relatively enormous openings which occupy the whole of the sides of the head. They are covered by a large operculum but this, in its turn, has attached to the middle of its inner face a transverse fold of skin which runs in a horizontal direction backwards through the ear opening to the wall of the cranium. This transverse fold divides the outer ear into two chambers, one of which is found to be "blind," with no con-nexion with the inner ear, whilst the other contains the true ear opening. In the ear on the right-hand side of the head (viewed from the back of the skull) the cavity containing the true ear-opening is the lower one, with the blind one on top; in the ear on the left-hand side however, the positions are exactly reversed, with the true ear opening uppermost. This remarkable asymmetry, which over-shadows in complexity that found in the tawny owl, is as baffling as it is extra-ordinary. Finally we come to Tengmalm's owl. In this bird the ears are very large and asymmetric, but the difference in shape between the right and left ears is so great that the skull has become lop-sided and is itself no longer symmetrical.

If the owls on the British list are arranged in order of their degree of nocturn-ality, they will be found to fall into three main classes, namely, those which are mainly diurnal, embracing the snowy owl, hawk-owl, and short-eared owl; those which are both diurnal and nocturnal, including the eagle-owl, little owl, scops-owl, and possibly the barn-owl; and those which are almost entirely nocturnal—the tawny owl, long-eared owl, and Tengmalm's owl. Apart from one notable exception, the complexity of their ears bears a broad direct relation-ship to the extent to which they hunt in the dark, the more nocturnal species having the more complex ears. But the parallelism is rendered almost useless from the point of view of interpreting the functions of the many modifications found in the ears of owls, by the position of the short-eared owl which, although one of the most diurnal of owls, has ears of a complexity very similar to those of its near but very nocturnal relative, the long-eared owl.

To sum up therefore, we can say that both the eyes and ears of owls have evolved along specialised lines, but that, whilst even the smallest modifications to the eye find a satisfactory interpretation in terms of adaptation to nocturnal conditions, the reasons for the many structural peculiarities in the ears of owls remain uninterpreted except on the broadest of bases.

Index